2017 SQA Specimen and Past Papers with Answers

National 5

LIFESKILLS MATHEMATICS

XSQA

National 5 LIFESKILLS MATHEMATICS

2016 & 2017 Exams
and 2017 Specimen Question Paper

This book contains the official SQA 2016 and 2017 Exams for National 5 Lifeskills Mathematics, and the 2017 Specimen Question Paper for National 5 Applications of Mathematics, with associated SQA-approved answers modified from the official marking instructions that accompany the paper.

In addition the book contains study skills advice. This advice has been specially commissioned by Hodder Gibson, and has been written by experienced senior teachers and examiners in line with the new National 5 syllabus and assessment outlines. This is not SQA material but has been devised to provide further guidance for National 5 examinations.

Hodder Gibson is grateful to the copyright holders, as credited on the final page of the Answer section, for permission to use their material. Every effort has been made to trace the copyright holders and to obtain their permission for the use of copyright material. Hodder Gibson will be happy to receive information allowing us to rectify any error or omission in future editions.

Hachette UK's policy is to use papers that are natural, renewable and recyclable products and made from wood grown in sustainable forests. The logging and manufacturing processes are expected to conform to the environmental regulations of the country of origin.

Orders: please contact Bookpoint Ltd, 130 Park Drive, Milton Park, Abingdon, Oxon OX14 4SE. Telephone: (44) 01235 827720. Fax: (44) 01235 400454. Lines are open 9.00–5.00, Monday to Saturday, with a 24-hour message answering service. Visit our website at www.hoddereducation.co.uk. Hodder Gibson can be contacted direct on: Tel: 0141 333 4650; Fax: 0141 404 8188; email: hoddergibson@hodder.co.uk

This collection first published in 2017 by
Hodder Gibson, an imprint of Hodder Education,
An Hachette UK Company
211 St Vincent Street
Glasgow G2 5QY

Typeset by Aptara, Inc.

Printed in the UK

A catalogue record for this title is available from the British Library

ISBN: 978-1-5104-2194-3

2 1

2018 2017

Introduction

National 5 Applications of Mathematics (formerly Lifeskills Mathematics)

This book of SQA Past Papers contains the actual 2016 and 2017 Question Papers (with answers at the back of the book). As the course specifications have changed, due to the removal of Unit Assessments and the 'strengthening' of the exams, a new Specimen Question Paper, which reflects the revised exam structure, is also included. The Specimen Question Paper reflects the content and duration of the exam in 2018. All of the question papers included in the book (2016, 2017 and the SQP) provide excellent practice for the final exams.

The 2016 and 2017 exams still provide excellent representative exam practice. Using them as part of your revision will help you to learn the vital skills and techniques needed for the exam, and will help you to identify any knowledge gaps you may have, prior to the exam season in May–June.

The course

The Applications of Mathematics (formerly Lifeskills Mathematics) course is a qualification which focuses on the application of mathematical skills in real-life contexts.

The National 5 Applications of Mathematics course aims to enable you to develop:

- a range of mathematical techniques and apply these to real-life problems or situations
- the ability to analyse a range of real-life problems or situations
- a confident and independent approach towards the use of mathematics in real-life situations
- the ability to select, apply and combine mathematical skills to new or unfamiliar situations in life and work
- the ability to use mathematical reasoning skills to generalise, support arguments, draw conclusions, assess risk and make informed decisions
- the ability to analyse, interpret and present a range of information
- the ability to communicate mathematical information in a variety of forms
- the ability to think creatively and in abstract ways.

Before starting this course you should already have the knowledge, understanding and skills required to achieve a pass in National 4 Applications of Mathematics and/or be proficient in appropriate experiences and outcomes.

This course enables you to further develop your knowledge, understanding, skills and reasoning processes in personal finance, statistics, geometry, measure, numeracy and data. The table outlines the topics covered in each area of the course:

<table>
<tr><th>Financial Skills</th><th>Statistical Skills</th><th>Numeracy Skills</th></tr>
<tr><td>Budgeting
Income and pay slips
Tax and deductions
Best deal
Currency conversion
Interest rates and saving/borrowing</td><td>Investigate probability/risk
Statistical diagrams
Analyse/compare data sets
Line of best fit</td><td rowspan="5">Select and use appropriate notation and units
Select and carry out operations including:
• working to given decimal places
• rounding to given significant figures
• fractions and mixed numbers
• percentages, including compound
• speed, distance, time
• area
• volume
• ratio
• proportion, direct and indirect</td></tr>
<tr><th>Geometrical Skills</th><th>Graphical Data and Probability Skills</th></tr>
<tr><td>Gradient
Composite shapes: Area
Composite solids: Volume
Pythagoras' theorem</td><td rowspan="3">Extract/interpret data from at least three different graphical forms
Make/justify decisions based on interpretation of data
Make/justify decisions based on probability</td></tr>
<tr><th>Measurement Skills</th></tr>
<tr><td>Scale drawing
Bearings
Container packing
Precedence tables
Time management
Tolerance</td></tr>
</table>

You will use your reasoning skills and the skills above, linked to real-life contexts. The amount of reasoning is what makes Applications of Mathematics different. You will be asked to analyse, compare, justify and communicate information.

Assessment

Course assessment for Applications of Mathematics is based on a final exam paper. The number of marks and the times allotted for the examination papers are as follows:

Paper 1 (non-calculator)	45 marks	1 hour and 5 minutes
Paper 2 (calculator allowed)	65 marks	2 hours

The Award is graded A–D, with the grade being determined by your performance in the exam, i.e. based on the total mark out of 110.

To achieve a grade C; you will typically have demonstrated **successful** performance in relation to the skills, knowledge and understanding of the course.

To achieve a grade A; you will typically have demonstrated a **consistently high level** of performance in relation to the skills, knowledge and understanding of the course.

Paper 1 consists of short-answer and extended-response questions, most of which are in context.

Paper 2 consists of short-answer questions, extended-response questions and **case studies**, most of which are in context. The time given to this Paper allows you to read and absorb the information in the case studies.

Some tips for achieving a good mark

- **DOING** maths questions is the most effective use of your study time. You will benefit much more from spending 30 minutes doing maths questions than spending several hours copying out notes or reading a maths textbook.
- Practise doing the types of questions that are likely to appear in the exam. Use the marking instructions to check your answers and to understand what the examiners are looking for. Ask your teacher for help if you get stuck.
- **SHOW ALL WORKING CLEARLY.** The instructions on the front of the exam paper state that *"Full credit will only be given where the solution contains appropriate working"*. A "correct" answer with no working may only be awarded partial marks or even no marks at all. An incomplete answer will be awarded marks for any appropriate working. Attempt every question, even if you are not sure whether you are correct or not. Your solution may contain working which will gain some marks. A blank response is certain to be awarded no marks. Never score out working unless you have something better to replace it with.
- Reasoning skills are a major part of Applications of Mathematics. One way of showing your reasoning process is by showing all of your working. Quite often you will be asked to *"Use your working to justify your answer"* – so you cannot just say "yes" or "no" without your working.
- Communication is very important in presenting solutions to questions. Diagrams are often a good way of conveying information and enabling markers to understand your working. Where a diagram is included in a question, it is often good practice to mark in any dimensions etc, which you work out and may use later.
- In Paper 1, you have to carry out calculations without a calculator. Ensure that you practise your number skills regularly, especially within questions that test course content. Also make sure that after you have calculated an answer you state the **units**, if appropriate. Paper 1 will be a mixture of short, medium and extended questions covering a single "skill", to three or four skills selected from the table on page 4. Most questions will be in context.
- In Paper 2, you will be allowed to use a calculator. Always use **your own** calculator. Different calculators often function in slightly different ways, so make sure that you know how to operate yours. Having to use a calculator that you are unfamiliar with on the day of the exam may cause frustration and loss of time. Paper 2 consists of short-answer questions, extended-response questions and case studies, most of which will be in context.
- Prepare thoroughly to tackle questions from **all** parts of the course. Always try all parts of a question. Just because you could not complete part (a), for example, this does not mean you could not do part (b) or (c).
- Look at how many **marks** are allocated to a question – this will give you an idea of how much work is required. The more marks, the more work!
- Look for **key words** in questions: state, calculate, compare, plot, sketch, draw, justify.

Some areas to consider

Each question is likely to have a mixture of strategy, process and communication marks.

You will be expected to:

- select a strategy (there may be more than one way to do a question)
- process the information (for example, carry out a calculation)
- communicate your answer (for example, "yes the company would accept as tolerance is within limits").

Here are some examples to consider:

Types of question	Things to consider
You may be asked to mark points on a scatter diagram, draw a line of best fit and then compare it with one already drawn.	Ensure points are **plotted accurately**. Try to make the **"slope"** of the line match points. Try to have about same number of points above and below the line of best fit.
You may be asked to make a scale drawing of, for example, a garden. You may then be asked to calculate measurements from this drawing.	Choose a scale which gives a good size, to fit the space given to you. **State the scale** you have used. Use this scale to calculate actual sizes. Remember to **state units**.
You may be asked to construct a box plot. You may have to compare this with one given.	Make sure you have a scale clearly marked. Make sure you mark in the **five-figure summary**. Valid comparison: 1 mark equals one comparison, 2 marks equal two comparison statements. For example, "plot 2 has a higher median and a greater spread". L Q1 Q2 Q3 H 10 15 20 25 30 35 40 45 50

In Paper 2 you have been given more time to allow you to read and absorb the information, particularly in the case studies.

You should take the opportunity to "settle into" the Paper by carefully working through the short-answer and extended-response questions. This will get you "thinking mathematically".

You should then look through the case studies to get a "feel" for what they are asking.

Case studies will typically "flow" through a context or scenario; developing the theme and assessing a variety of skills, knowledge and understanding. The case studies will vary in length; some assessing one, or one or two skills, whilst longer ones will test a number of skills across the range of skills in the course.

Typically you will be given a context and have to answer a question or two on the information given. You may then be given more information in order that the case study may develop and you will have another part of the question to answer. In this way you should be able to build up your answers and, therefore, your marks as you progress through the case study.

Remember, even if you could not answer, say, part (b) – always look at part (c) to see if you can answer that part.

Good luck!

Remember that the rewards for passing National 5 Applications of Mathematics are well worth it! Your pass will help you get the future you want for yourself. In the exam, be confident in your own ability. If you're not sure how to answer a question, trust your instincts and just give it a go anyway. Keep calm and don't panic! GOOD LUCK!

Study Skills – what you need to know to pass exams!

Pause for thought

Many students might skip quickly through a page like this. After all, we all know how to revise. Do you really though?

Think about this:

"IF YOU ALWAYS DO WHAT YOU ALWAYS DO, YOU WILL ALWAYS GET WHAT YOU HAVE ALWAYS GOT."

Do you like the grades you get? Do you want to do better? If you get full marks in your assessment, then that's great! Change nothing! This section is just to help you get that little bit better than you already are.

There are two main parts to the advice on offer here. The first part highlights fairly obvious things but which are also very important. The second part makes suggestions about revision that you might not have thought about but which WILL help you.

Part 1

DOH! It's so obvious but …

Start revising in good time

Don't leave it until the last minute – this will make you panic.

Make a revision timetable that sets out work time AND play time.

Sleep and eat!

Obvious really, and very helpful. Avoid arguments or stressful things too – even games that wind you up. You need to be fit, awake and focused!

Know your place!

Make sure you know exactly **WHEN and WHERE** your exams are.

Know your enemy!

Make sure you know what to expect in the exam.

How is the paper structured?

How much time is there for each question?

What types of question are involved?

Which topics seem to come up time and time again?

Which topics are your strongest and which are your weakest?

Are all topics compulsory or are there choices?

Learn by DOING!

There is no substitute for past papers and practice papers – they are simply essential! Tackling this collection of papers and answers is exactly the right thing to be doing as your exams approach.

Part 2

People learn in different ways. Some like low light, some bright. Some like early morning, some like evening / night. Some prefer warm, some prefer cold. But everyone uses their BRAIN and the brain works when it is active. Passive learning – sitting gazing at notes – is the most INEFFICIENT way to learn anything. Below you will find tips and ideas for making your revision more effective and maybe even more enjoyable. What follows gets your brain active, and active learning works!

Activity 1 – Stop and review

Step 1

When you have done no more than 5 minutes of revision reading STOP!

Step 2

Write a heading in your own words which sums up the topic you have been revising.

Step 3

Write a summary of what you have revised in no more than two sentences. Don't fool yourself by saying, "I know it, but I cannot put it into words". That just means you don't know it well enough. If you cannot write your summary, revise that section again, knowing that you must write a summary at the end of it. Many of you will have notebooks full of blue/black ink writing. Many of the pages will not be especially attractive or memorable so try to liven them up a bit with colour as you are reviewing and rewriting. **This is a great memory aid, and memory is the most important thing.**

Activity 2 – Use technology!

Why should everything be written down? Have you thought about "mental" maps, diagrams, cartoons and colour to help you learn? And rather than write down notes, why not record your revision material?

What about having a text message revision session with friends? Keep in touch with them to find out how and what they are revising and share ideas and questions.

Why not make a video diary where you tell the camera what you are doing, what you think you have learned and what you still have to do? No one has to see or hear it, but the process of having to organise your thoughts in a formal way to explain something is a very important learning practice.

Be sure to make use of electronic files. You could begin to summarise your class notes. Your typing might be slow, but it will get faster and the typed notes will be easier to read than the scribbles in your class notes. Try to add different fonts and colours to make your work stand out. You can easily Google relevant pictures, cartoons and diagrams which you can copy and paste to make your work more attractive and **MEMORABLE**.

Activity 3 – This is it. Do this and you will know lots!

Step 1

In this task you must be very honest with yourself! Find the SQA syllabus for your subject (www.sqa.org.uk). Look at how it is broken down into main topics called MANDATORY knowledge. That means stuff you MUST know.

Step 2

BEFORE you do ANY revision on this topic, write a list of everything that you already know about the subject. It might be quite a long list but you only need to write it once. It shows you all the information that is already in your long-term memory so you know what parts you do not need to revise!

Step 3

Pick a chapter or section from your book or revision notes. Choose a fairly large section or a whole chapter to get the most out of this activity.

With a buddy, use Skype, Facetime, Twitter or any other communication you have, to play the game "If this is the answer, what is the question?". For example, if you are revising Geography and the answer you provide is "meander", your buddy would have to make up a question like "What is the word that describes a feature of a river where it flows slowly and bends often from side to side?".

Make up 10 "answers" based on the content of the chapter or section you are using. Give this to your buddy to solve while you solve theirs.

Step 4

Construct a wordsearch of at least 10 × 10 squares. You can make it as big as you like but keep it realistic. Work together with a group of friends. Many apps allow you to make wordsearch puzzles online. The words and phrases can go in any direction and phrases can be split. Your puzzle must only contain facts linked to the topic you are revising. Your task is to find 10 bits of information to hide in your puzzle, but you must not repeat information that you used in Step 3. DO NOT show where the words are. Fill up empty squares with random letters. Remember to keep a note of where your answers are hidden but do not show your friends. When you have a complete puzzle, exchange it with a friend to solve each other's puzzle.

Step 5

Now make up 10 questions (not "answers" this time) based on the same chapter used in the previous two tasks. Again, you must find NEW information that you have not yet used. Now it's getting hard to find that new information! Again, give your questions to a friend to answer.

Step 6

As you have been doing the puzzles, your brain has been actively searching for new information. Now write a NEW LIST that contains only the new information you have discovered when doing the puzzles. Your new list is the one to look at repeatedly for short bursts over the next few days. Try to remember more and more of it without looking at it. After a few days, you should be able to add words from your second list to your first list as you increase the information in your long-term memory.

FINALLY! Be inspired...

Make a list of different revision ideas and beside each one write **THINGS I HAVE** tried, **THINGS I WILL** try and **THINGS I MIGHT** try. Don't be scared of trying something new.

And remember – "FAIL TO PREPARE AND PREPARE TO FAIL!"

NATIONAL 5

2016

FOR OFFICIAL USE

N5 National Qualifications 2016

Mark

X744/75/01

Lifeskills Mathematics Paper 1 (Non-Calculator)

WEDNESDAY, 4 MAY

9:00 AM — 9:50 AM

Fill in these boxes and read what is printed below.

Full name of centre

Town

Forename(s)

Surname

Number of seat

Date of birth

Day Month Year

Scottish candidate number

Total marks — 35

Attempt ALL questions.

You may NOT use a calculator.

Full credit will be given only to solutions which contain appropriate working.

State the units for your answer where appropriate.

Write your answers clearly in the spaces provided in this booklet. Additional space for answers is provided at the end of this booklet. If you use this space you must clearly identify the question number you are attempting.

Use **blue** or **black** ink.

Before leaving the examination room you must give this booklet to the Invigilator; if you do not, you may lose all the marks for this paper.

FORMULAE LIST

Circumference of a circle: $C = \pi d$

Area of a circle: $A = \pi r^2$

Theorem of Pythagoras:

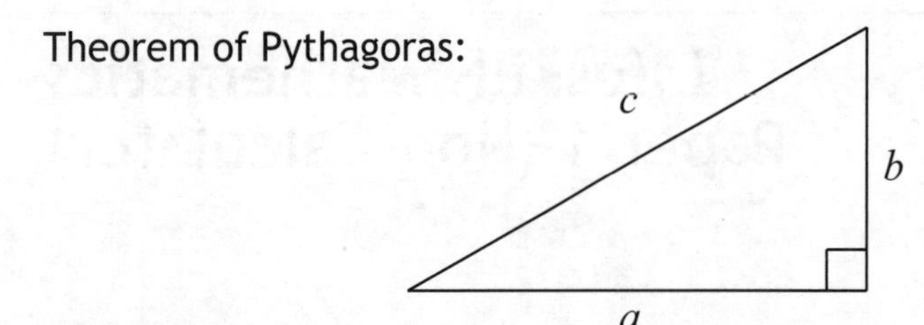

$a^2 \quad b^2 \quad c^2$

Volume of a cylinder: $V = \pi r^2 h$

Volume of a prism: $V = Ah$

Volume of a cone: $V = \frac{1}{3}\pi r^2 h$

Volume of a sphere: $V = \frac{4}{3}\pi r^3$

Standard deviation: $s = \sqrt{\frac{\Sigma(x - \overline{x})^2}{n-1}} = \sqrt{\frac{\Sigma x^2 - (\Sigma x)^2/n}{n-1}}$, where n is the sample size.

Gradient:

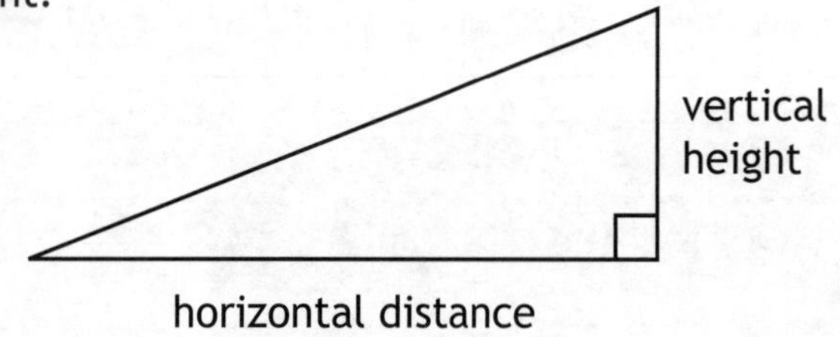

$$\text{gradient} = \frac{\text{vertical height}}{\text{horizontal distance}}$$

MARKS DO NOT WRITE IN THIS MARGIN

Total marks — 35

Attempt ALL questions

1. A restaurant can buy long grain rice in two sizes of bags.

- A 9 kg bag costs £25·65
- A 20 kg bag costs £57·20

Which size of bag is better value for the restaurant?

Use your working to justify your answer. 3

2. Aneesha and Brian are playing a board game. Each move is determined by rolling two dice.

Aneesha requires a total of **10 or more** on her next roll to win the game.

What is the probability of Aneesha winning the game on the next roll?

Give your answer as a fraction. 3

[Turn over

MARKS | DO NOT WRITE IN THIS MARGIN

3. Gary lives in Biggar and has to go to a meeting in Edinburgh.

He plans to travel to his meeting by bus.

He uses this bus timetable to plan his journey.

Dumfries • Biggar • Edinburgh

Monday to Friday

Route Number	101	101	101	101	101	102	101	101	101	101	101	102
Dumfries Whitesands Stance 4		**0535**	**0710**		**0910**	**1025**			**1315**			**1815**
Heathhall		0543	0720		0920	|			1325			|
Amisfield Main Rd		0547	0725		0925	|			1330			|
Parkgate		0552	0730		0930	|			1335			|
St Ann's		0557	0736		0936	|			1341			|
Beattock Primary School		0606	0745		0945	|			1350			|
Moffat High St Stance 2		**0612**	**0752**		**0952**	|			**1357**			|
Holywood		|	|		|	1031			|			1821
Auldgirth		|	|		|	1039			|			1829
Closeburn		|	|		|	1046			|			1836
Thornhill Cross		|	|		|	1050			|			1840
Durisdeermill		|	|		|	1100			|			1850
Troloss		|	|		|	1105			|			1855
Elvanfoot		|	|		|	1117			|			1907
Crawford		0633	0813		1013	1128			1418			1913
Abington Village		0640	0820		1020	1135			1425			1920
Abington Service Area		0646	0827		1027	1142			1432			1927
Roberton		0651	0832		1032	1147			1437			1932
Lamington		0657	0838		1038	1153			1443			1938
Coulter		0702	0843		1043	1158			1448			1943
Biggar	**0633**	**0709**	**0853**	**0953**	**1053**	**1208**	**1253**	**1353**	**1458**	**1623**	**1803**	**1953**
Dolphinton	0644	0721	0905	1004	1104	1219	1304	1404	1509	1634	1814	2004
West Linton	0651	0731	0915	1011	1111	1226	1311	1411	1516	1641	1821	2011
Carlops	0655	0735	0920	1015	1115	1230	1315	1415	1520	1645	1825	2015
Silverburn	0702	0741	0927	1021	1121	1236	1321	1421	1526	1651	1831	2021
Penicuik Town Centre Stop C	0707	|	0932	1026	|	1241	1326	1426	|	1656	1836	2026
Flotterstone	0717	0746	0942	1036	1126	1251	1336	1436	1531	1706	1846	2034
Fairmilehead, Swanston Drive	0724	0753	0948	1042	1132	1257	1342	1442	1537	1712	1852	2039
Morningside Station	0732	0801	0956	1050	1140	1305	1350	1450	1545	1720	1900	2045
Tollcross	0740	0809	1004	1058	1148	1313	1358	1458	1553	1728	1908	2050
Lothian Road, Caledonian Hotel	0749	0818	1011	1104	1154	1319	1404	1504	1600	1735	1914	2055
Edinburgh Bus Stance E	**0801**	**0830**	**1021**	**1114**	**1204**	**1329**	**1414**	**1514**	**1611**	**1745**	**1924**	**2102**

His meeting in Edinburgh starts at 11:30 am.

It will take him 25 minutes to walk from the Edinburgh bus stance to his meeting.

What is the latest bus he can catch in Biggar to be at his meeting on time? **2**

MARKS | DO NOT WRITE IN THIS MARGIN

4. Seonaid is saving up to buy a tablet computer costing £388.

She earns £7·30 per hour and works for 30 hours each week.

Seonaid is paid at the end of each week.

She pays £5·32 in Income Tax and £7·68 in National Insurance each week.

Her living expenses are £86 per week.

Seonaid saves **half** of the money that she has left each week towards the tablet computer.

How many weeks will it take her to save up enough money to buy the computer? **3**

[Turn over

MARKS | DO NOT WRITE IN THIS MARGIN

5. A computer company is researching how long it would take to develop a new games console and bring it to market.

The following table of necessary tasks was produced.

Activity	Description	Preceding Task	Time (months)
A	Product design	None	12
B	Market research	None	2
C	Production analysis	A	3
D	Product model	A	4
E	Sales brochure	A	1
F	Product testing	D	5
G	Cost analysis	C	3
H	Sales training	B,E	2
I	Pricing	H	1
J	Project report	F,G,I	1

(a) Complete the diagram below to show the tasks and times in the boxes. (An additional diagram, if required, can be found on *Page twelve*). **2**

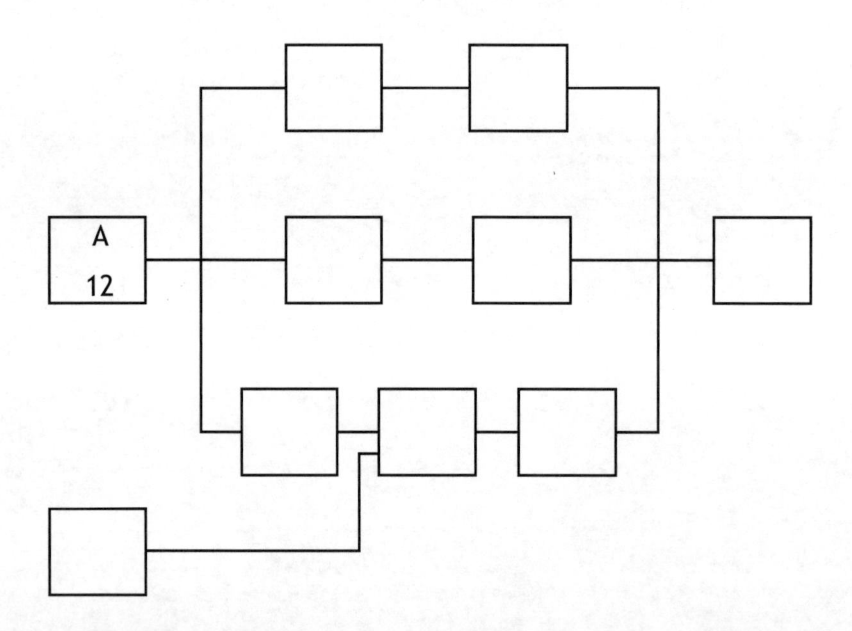

(b) The company want this entire process to be completed in 2 years.

Based on the times given, is this possible?

Show working to justify your answer. **2**

MARKS DO NOT WRITE IN THIS MARGIN

6. A farmer needs to **completely enclose** this field with a new fence.

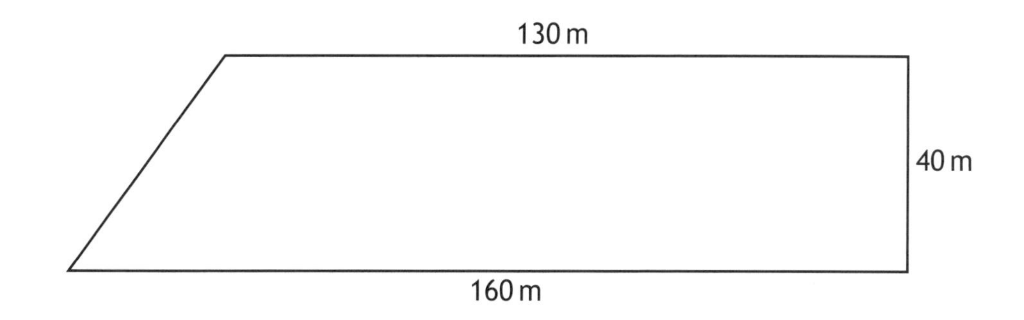

The fence is only sold in 80 metre rolls.

Each roll costs £73·99.

Calculate the cost of the new fence. **5**

[Turn over

7. The table below shows the vehicle tax to be paid on different vehicles.

The amount of vehicle tax paid depends on the CO_2 emissions of the vehicle and the fuel type.

Standard Rates - The following table contains the rates of vehicle tax for already registered cars, based on CO_2 emissions and fuel type.

		Petrol Car (Tax Class 48) and Diesel Car (Tax Class 49)				
		Non Direct Debit		Direct Debit		
Bands	CO_2 emission figure (g/km)	12 months	Six months	Single 12 month payment	Total payable by 12 monthly instalments	Single six month payment
Band A	Up to 100	£0	-	-	-	-
Band B	101 to 110	£20	-	£20	£21	-
Band C	111 to 120	£30	-	£30	£31·50	-
Band D	121 to 130	£110	£60·50	£110	£115·50	£57·75
Band E	131 to 140	£130	£71·50	£130	£136·50	£68·25
Band F	141 to 150	£145	£79·75	£145	£152·25	£76·13
Band G	151 to 165	£180	£99	£180	£189	£94·50
Band H	166 to 175	£205	£112·75	£205	£215·25	£107·63
Band I	176 to 185	£225	£123·75	£225	£236·25	£118·13
Band J	186 to 200	£265	£145·75	£265	£278·25	£139·13
Band K	201 to 225	£290	£159·50	£290	£304·50	£152·25
Band L	226 to 255	£490	£269·50	£490	£514·50	£257·25
Band M	Over 255	£505	£277·75	£505	£530·25	£265·13

MARKS DO NOT WRITE IN THIS MARGIN

Tom buys a **petrol** car which has a CO_2 emission figure of 142 g/km.

Tom decides to pay his vehicle tax by direct debit in two single six month payments.

How much more expensive is this than a single 12 month payment by direct debit? **3**

MARKS | DO NOT WRITE IN THIS MARGIN

8. A new playground is planned for Aberbeath Primary School.

It will be a rectangle measuring 19 metres by 8 metres.

A semi-circular sandpit will be built within the playground as shown

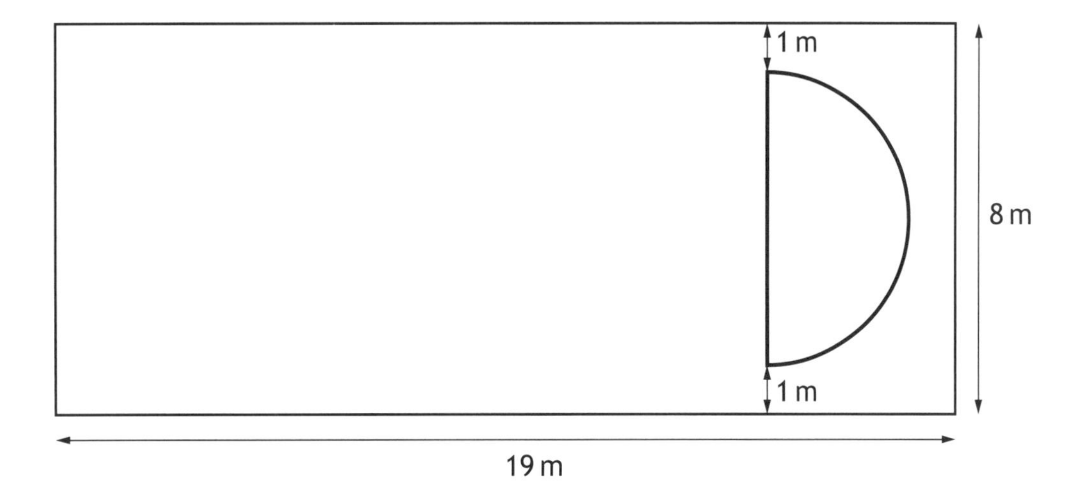

The playground, excluding the sandpit, is to be covered in rubber tiles.

Calculate the area to be covered by the rubber tiles.

Take $\pi = 3 \cdot 14$.

Give your answer to **3 significant figures**. 4

[Turn over

MARKS DO NOT WRITE IN THIS MARGIN

9. A picture is glued onto a piece of card as shown.

- The picture is a rectangle with dimensions 4 cm by 5 cm.
- The rectangular card has an **area** 2·8 times greater than the **area** of the picture.
- One of the dimensions of the piece of card is 7 cm.

Calculate the other dimension of the piece of card. **3**

MARKS | DO NOT WRITE IN THIS MARGIN

10. Bradley decides to cycle from Kilsyth to the highest point of Tak-Ma-Doon Road.

- The horizontal distance between these two places is 4·5 kilometres.
- Kilsyth is 70 metres above sea level.
- The highest point of Tak-Ma-Doon Road is 320 metres above sea level.

(a) Calculate the average gradient between Kilsyth and the highest point of Tak-Ma-Doon Road.

Give your answer as a fraction **in its simplest form**. **3**

(b) One part of the road has gradient $\frac{2}{25}$.

Is this steeper than the average gradient?

You must justify your answer. **2**

[END OF QUESTION PAPER]

MARKS | DO NOT WRITE IN THIS MARGIN

ADDITIONAL SPACE FOR ANSWERS

Additional diagram for Question 5 (a)

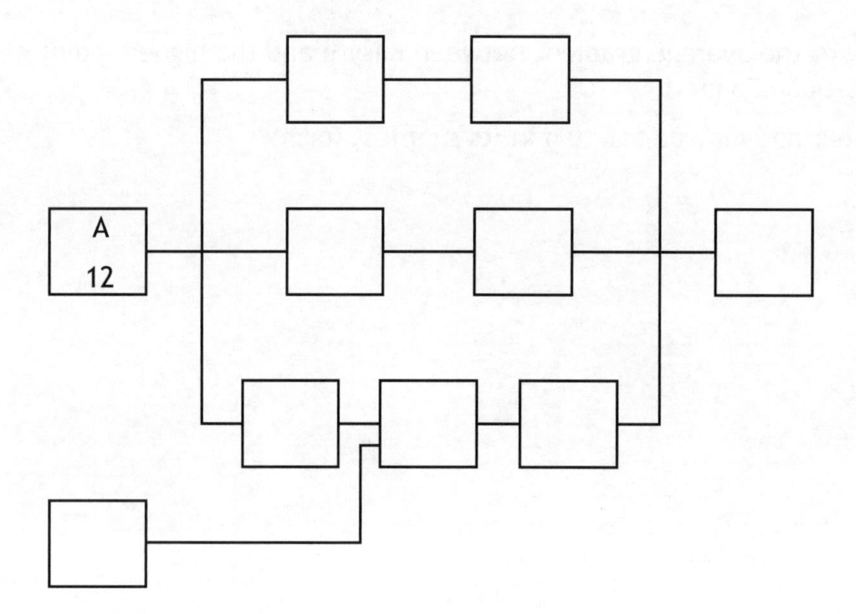

MARKS DO NOT WRITE IN THIS MARGIN

ADDITIONAL SPACE FOR ANSWERS

MARKS | DO NOT WRITE IN THIS MARGIN

ADDITIONAL SPACE FOR ANSWERS

FOR OFFICIAL USE

N5

National Qualifications 2016

Mark

X744/75/02

Lifeskills Mathematics Paper 2

WEDNESDAY, 4 MAY

10:10 AM – 11:50 AM

Fill in these boxes and read what is printed below.

Full name of centre

Town

Forename(s)

Surname

Number of seat

Date of birth

Day Month Year

Scottish candidate number

Total marks — 55

Attempt ALL questions.

You may use a calculator.

Full credit will be given only to solutions which contain appropriate working.

State the units for your answer where appropriate.

Write your answers clearly in the spaces provided in this booklet. Additional space for answers is provided at the end of this booklet. If you use this space you must clearly identify the question number you are attempting.

Use **blue** or **black** ink.

Before leaving the examination room you must give this book to the Invigilator; if you do not, you may lose all the marks for this paper.

FORMULAE LIST

Circumference of a circle: $C = \pi d$

Area of a circle: $A = \pi r^2$

Theorem of Pythagoras:

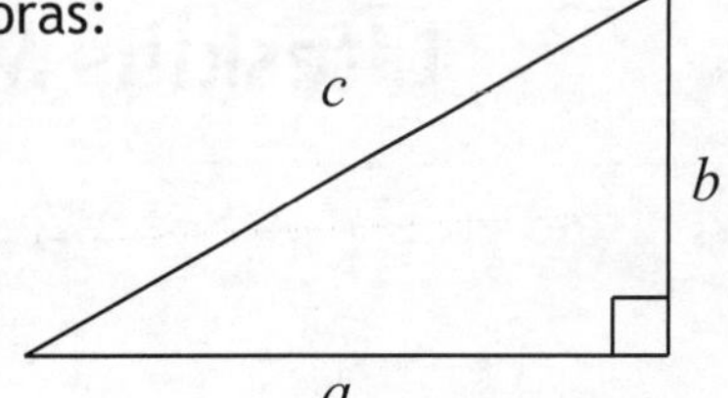

$a^2 \quad b^2 \quad c^2$

Volume of a cylinder: $V = \pi r^2 h$

Volume of a prism: $V = Ah$

Volume of a cone: $V = \frac{1}{3}\pi r^2 h$

Volume of a sphere: $V = \frac{4}{3}\pi r^3$

Standard deviation: $s = \sqrt{\frac{\Sigma(x-\bar{x})^2}{n-1}} = \sqrt{\frac{\Sigma x^2 - (\Sigma x)^2/n}{n-1}}$, where n is the sample size.

Gradient:

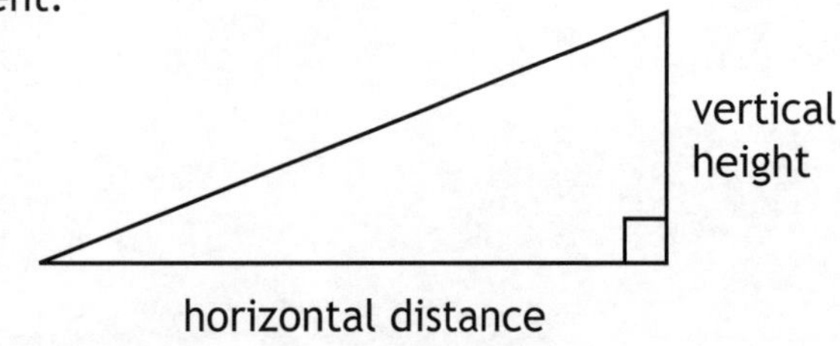

$$\text{gradient} = \frac{\text{vertical height}}{\text{horizontal distance}}$$

MARKS DO NOT WRITE IN THIS MARGIN

Total marks — 55

Attempt ALL questions

1. The population of Scotland is recorded to the nearest hundred.

   In 2014, the population was 5 347 600.

   In 2015, the population was 5 369 000.

   (a) Show that the percentage growth in population from 2014 to 2015 was 0·4%. **2**

   (b) If the population continues to grow at the same rate, calculate the expected population in 2018.

   Give your answer to the **nearest hundred**. **3**

[Turn over

MARKS | DO NOT WRITE IN THIS MARGIN

2. Chris flew from Perth, Australia, to London, United Kingdom, on Saturday 9th January 2016.

- The plane left Perth, Australia, at 13:05.
- The total journey time, including a stopover in Dubai, is 20 hours and 25 minutes.
- Perth time is 8 hours ahead of London.

At what time did the plane land in London? **2**

MARKS DO NOT WRITE IN THIS MARGIN

3. In September 2014 there was a referendum to determine the future of Scotland.

An opinion poll was taken in December 2013.
The question asked was “Should Scotland be an independent country?”

The results are shown in the pie chart below.

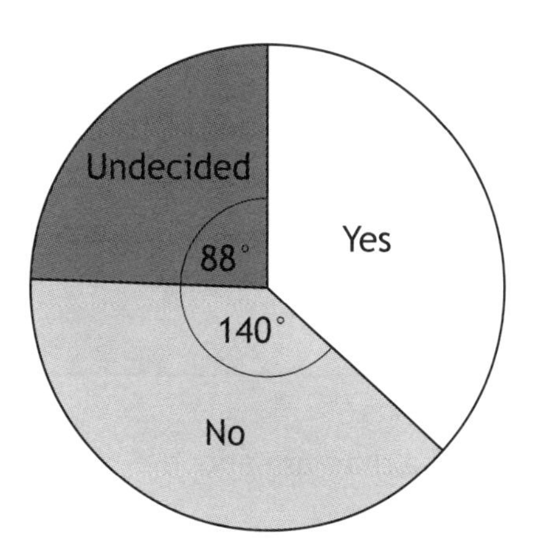

Another opinion poll was taken in April 2014.
1208 people were asked the same question as in December 2013.

The results of this poll are shown in the table below.

YES	NO	UNDECIDED
447	616	145

Compare the two opinion polls and make one relevant comment on the differences between them. **3**

[Turn over

MARKS DO NOT WRITE IN THIS MARGIN

4. Alison and Michael are travelling to Inverie on Knoydart for a holiday. They must take a ferry from Mallaig to Inverie

(a) The direct distance from Mallaig to Inverie is 9·8 kilometres.

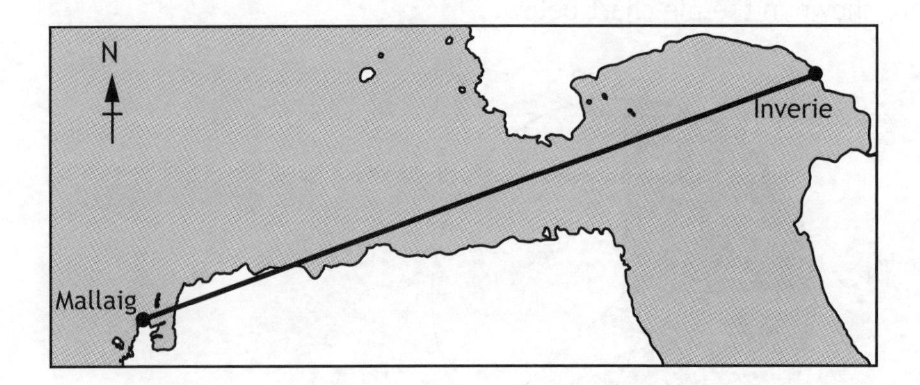

(i) Calculate the scale used in the diagram above. 1

(ii)

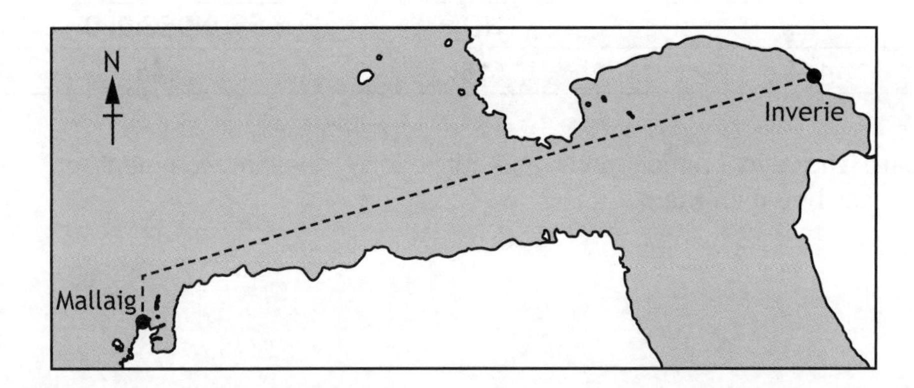

The ferry leaves Mallaig and travels North for 0·6 km.

The ferry then changes direction to sail directly to Inverie.

Use the second diagram to find the bearing and distance, in kilometres, that the ferry must travel on the **second part** of its journey. 2

MARKS | DO NOT WRITE IN THIS MARGIN

4. (continued)

(b) The average speed of the ferry from Mallaig to Inverie is 24 ± 3 kilometres per hour depending on tide and weather.

What is the shortest time that the **complete** ferry journey might take?

Give your answer to the **nearest minute**. 3

[Turn over

MARKS | DO NOT WRITE IN THIS MARGIN

5. Fiona is planning to stay in New York, USA, for three days.
She researches the cost of various attractions.

Attraction	Full price in US Dollars
Empire State Building	$32
Top of the Rock Observation Deck	$30
Statue of Liberty Cruise	$40
9/11 Memorial and Museum	$24
Waxworks	$37
One World Observatory	$32

Fiona will visit all six of these attractions while she is there.

Fiona plans to buy a discount card to reduce the cost of visiting these attractions.

Not all of the attractions are included in all of the cards. Fiona must pay full price for these.

Card 1: NY Card

NY Card

Attractions:

★ Sea and Space Museum ★ ★ Top of the Rock Observation Deck ★
★ Museum of Natural History ★ ★ 9/11 Memorial and Museum ★
★ Statue of Liberty Cruise ★ ★ Empire State Building ★

★★★★ Total Cost $114 ★★★★

Benefits:

These six attractions can be visited for a single payment of $114.
This card can only be used once per attraction.
It is valid for 30 days from first use.

Card 2: Explore NY Card

Explore NY Card

Attractions:

9/11 Memorial and Museum • Statue of Liberty Cruise
Museum of Natural History • Sea and Space Museum
Empire State Building • Top of the Rock Observation Deck
Waxworks • Carnegie Hall • Rockefeller Centre Tour

Cost for any 3 attractions $71

Benefits:

This card can be used for any 3 attractions from the list.
This card can only be used once per attraction.
It is valid for 30 days from first use.

MARKS | DO NOT WRITE IN THIS MARGIN

5. (continued)

Card 3: NY Town Pass

Benefits:

All of Fiona's chosen attractions can be visited with this card.

(a) During her three-day visit, Fiona will visit two attractions each day.

Fiona is going to buy one discount card.

(i) Calculate the total cost of all six attractions if Fiona buys Card 1. **2**

(ii) Calculate the cheapest price that Fiona could pay for entry to her six chosen attractions. **4**

(b) Fiona pays the cheapest price for entry to her six chosen attractions.

She pays before leaving the UK.

The cost is £100·96.

Calculate the exchange rate that Fiona received.

Give your answer correct to **3 decimal places.** **2**

[Turn over

MARKS | DO NOT WRITE IN THIS MARGIN

6. Fraser tests motorcycle tyres on racing circuits.

On Monday he tested Goodhold tyres.

His lap times, in seconds, are given below.

81·8 81·7 81·6 81·0 80·3 80·2

(a) For Fraser's times on Goodhold tyres, calculate:

(i) the mean; **1**

(ii) the standard deviation. **3**

MARKS | DO NOT WRITE IN THIS MARGIN

6. (continued)

(b) Fraser then changed to Megagrip tyres and recorded his times for another six laps.

These times produced a mean of 81·6 seconds and standard deviation of 0·65 seconds.

Make two valid comments comparing the two types of tyres. **2**

(c) Another rider completed one lap of the circuit in 81·0 seconds.

The track is 3·6 kilometres long.

Calculate his average speed in **kilometres per hour.** **3**

[Turn over

MARKS | DO NOT WRITE IN THIS MARGIN

7. Grace works for a company selling fitted kitchens.

She is paid a basic monthly salary of £500.

She also receives 5% commission on all her sales **above** £8000.

In January Grace sells £23 000 of goods.

Her monthly deductions are 12% of her gross income.

Grace writes down her budget for the month.

Rent	£245
Bills	£198
Food	£164
Entertaining	£75

Grace saves any surplus.

(a) Calculate Grace's **net** pay for January. 4

(b) (i) Calculate the surplus that Grace will have for January. 1

(ii) Grace's rent increases to £260 per month.

Calculate the percentage increase in her rent. 2

MARKS | DO NOT WRITE IN THIS MARGIN

7. (continued)

(c) To buy a car Grace needs to borrow £4500.

She wants to repay the loan **as soon as possible.**

She investigates the cost of the loan from five different lenders.

The table shows the repayments for a £4500 loan.

Lender	12 months	24 months	36 months
Tasko	£413·86	£215·07	£150·60
Bank of Shapes	£418·54	£219·31	£157·42
TMS	£458·83	£260·59	£197·74
Premier Bank	£422·46	£214·74	£159·21
Free Bank	£432·99	£234·15	£170·09

Grace assumes that she will earn the same commission each month.

Calculate her **new monthly surplus** and determine from which lender she should take her loan, and over how many months. **2**

[Turn over

MARKS | DO NOT WRITE IN THIS MARGIN

8. Brendan makes candles from blocks of wax.

Each block of wax is a cuboid measuring 30 cm by 20 cm by 20 cm as shown.

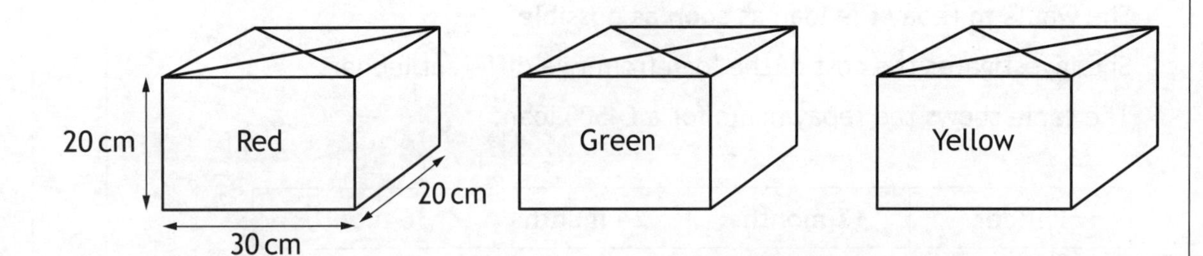

Each candle contains the colours red, green and yellow in the ratio 3 : 1 : 2 respectively.

Each candle is a cube with volume 729 cm^3.

(a) Brendan only has 1 block of each colour.
What is the maximum number of candles that he can make? **3**

Brendan makes the maximum number of candles.
Any wax that is left over is thrown away.

Each block of wax costs £13·75.
Brendan also buys wicks which cost 18p per candle.

Brendan adds 65% to his costs when calculating the selling price of each candle.

(b) What is Brendan's selling price for each candle? **3**

MARKS DO NOT WRITE IN THIS MARGIN

8. (continued)

Brendan also makes blue candles in the shape of a cylinder with a cone on top as shown.

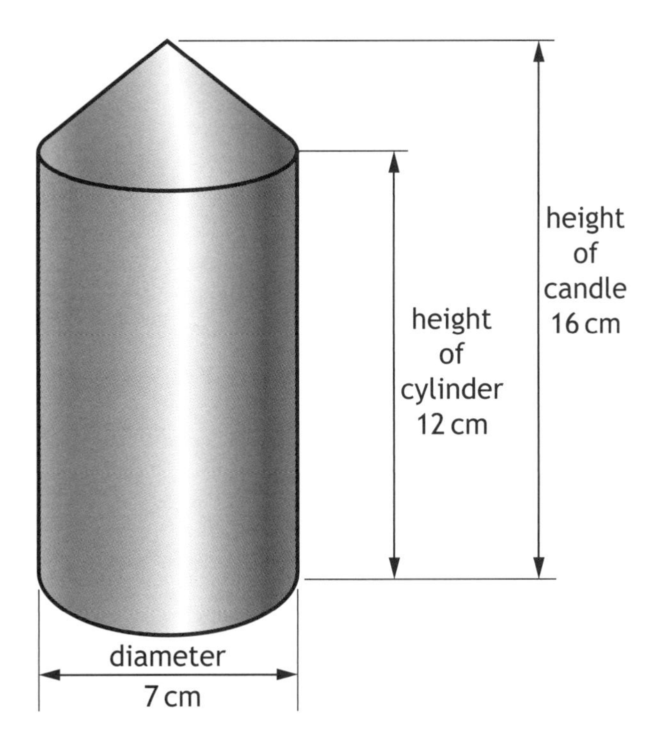

(c) He buys blue wax in blocks with volume 12 000 cm^3.

Brendan thinks that he can make 25 of these candles from one block of wax.

Is he correct?

Use your working to justify your answer. **7**

[END OF QUESTION PAPER]

MARKS | DO NOT WRITE IN THIS MARGIN

ADDITIONAL SPACE FOR ANSWERS

MARKS | DO NOT WRITE IN THIS MARGIN

ADDITIONAL SPACE FOR ANSWERS

MARKS DO NOT WRITE IN THIS MARGIN

ADDITIONAL SPACE FOR ANSWERS

MARKS | DO NOT WRITE IN THIS MARGIN

ADDITIONAL SPACE FOR ANSWERS

MARKS DO NOT WRITE IN THIS MARGIN

ADDITIONAL SPACE FOR ANSWERS

NATIONAL 5

2017

FOR OFFICIAL USE

N5 National Qualifications 2017

Mark

X744/75/01

Lifeskills Mathematics Paper 1 (Non-Calculator)

MONDAY, 29 MAY

1:00 PM — 1:50 PM

Fill in these boxes and read what is printed below.

Full name of centre

Town

Forename(s)

Surname

Number of seat

Date of birth

Day Month Year

Scottish candidate number

Total marks — 35

Attempt ALL questions.

You may NOT use a calculator.

Full credit will be given only to solutions which contain appropriate working.

State the units for your answer where appropriate.

Write your answers clearly in the spaces provided in this booklet. Additional space for answers is provided at the end of this booklet. If you use this space you must clearly identify the question number you are attempting.

Use **blue** or **black** ink.

Before leaving the examination room you must give this book to the Invigilator; if you do not, you may lose all the marks for this paper.

FORMULAE LIST

Circumference of a circle: $C = \pi d$

Area of a circle: $A = \pi r^2$

Theorem of Pythagoras:

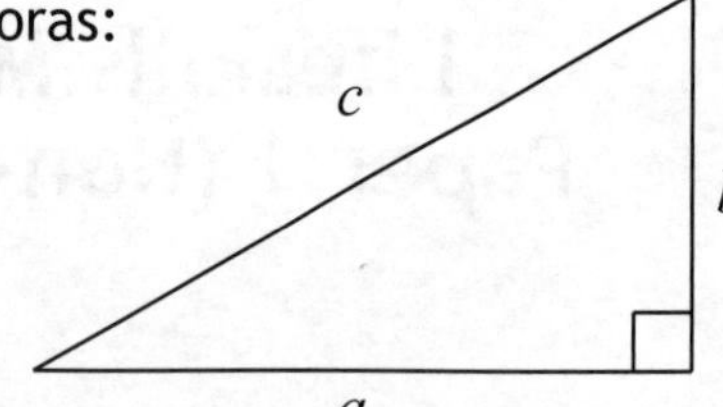

$a^2 \quad b^2 \quad c^2$

Volume of a cylinder: $V = \pi r^2 h$

Volume of a prism: $V = Ah$

Volume of a cone: $V = \frac{1}{3}\pi r^2 h$

Volume of a sphere: $V = \frac{4}{3}\pi r^3$

Standard deviation: $s = \sqrt{\frac{\Sigma(x-\overline{x})^2}{n-1}} = \sqrt{\frac{\Sigma x^2 - (\Sigma x)^2/n}{n-1}}$, where n is the sample size.

Gradient:

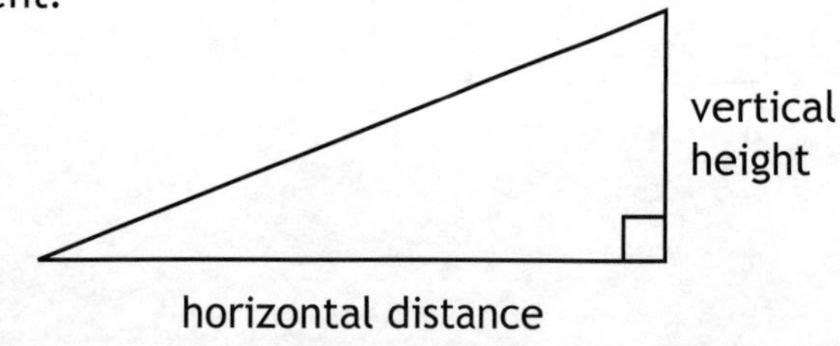

$$\text{gradient} = \frac{\text{vertical height}}{\text{horizontal distance}}$$

MARKS | DO NOT WRITE IN THIS MARGIN

Total marks — 35

Attempt ALL questions

1. A wall is built using foam bricks which are 194 ± 2 mm long.

The wall is 50 bricks long.

What is the minimum length of the wall? **2**

2. Anna works as a sales person for a computer company.

She is paid a basic monthly salary of £2450 plus commission of 2·5% on her monthly sales over £3000.

(a) Calculate Anna's gross salary for April when her sales totalled £9000. **3**

In her April payslip, she has the following deductions:

- Income Tax £334·67
- National Insurance £230·20
- Pension £164·74

(b) Calculate her net salary for April. **2**

MARKS | DO NOT WRITE IN THIS MARGIN

3. Scott is a farmer.

He records the weight of a calf from birth.

The weight of his calf is shown in the table below.

Days after birth	0	60	120	160	200	260
Weight (kg)	40	110	130	175	220	275

(a) On the grid below draw a scatter graph to show this data. **2**

(An additional grid, if required, can be found on *Page fourteen*.)

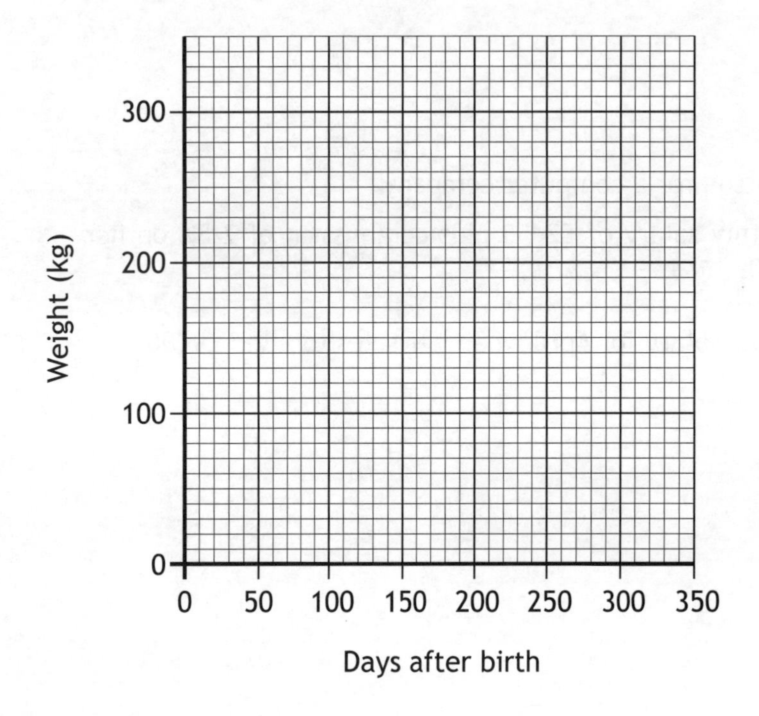

(b) Draw a line of best fit on the diagram above. **1**

(c) Use your line of best fit to estimate the **age** of this calf in days when it weighed 240 kilograms. **1**

MARKS DO NOT WRITE IN THIS MARGIN

4. When classifying mountain bike trails, the gradient of the steepest section is taken into account.

Colour Grade (Difficulty)	Maximum Gradient
Green (Easy)	$\frac{1}{10}$
Blue (Intermediate)	$\frac{3}{20}$
Red (Advanced)	$\frac{1}{4}$
Black (Severe)	$\frac{1}{2}$

A new trail has been built at a mountain bike centre.

The steepest section of the new trail is shown below.

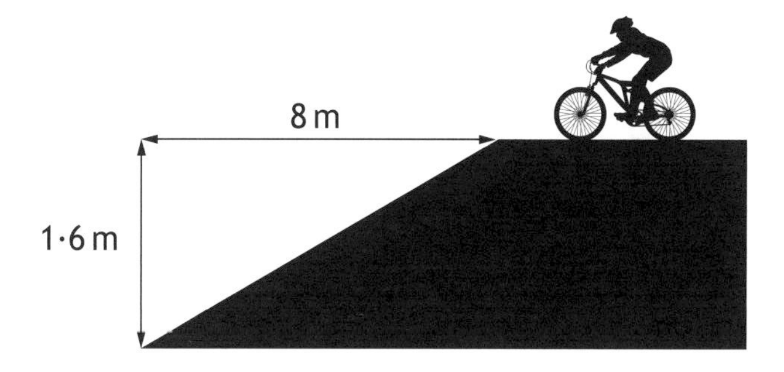

Can this be classified as a blue trail? 3

Use your working to justify your answer.

MARKS | DO NOT WRITE IN THIS MARGIN

5. Jane is trying to improve the number of pull ups she can do.

She looks online for pull up assistance bands.

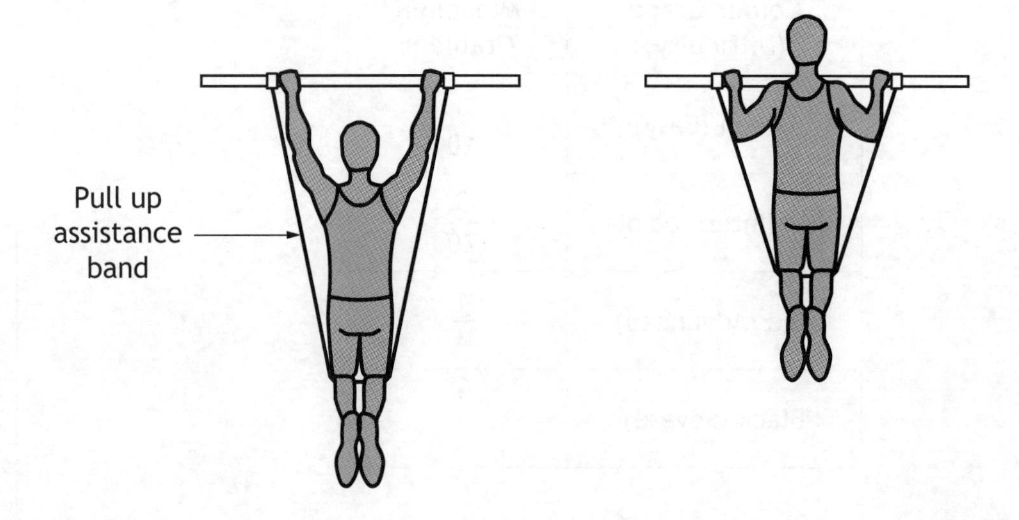

Jane finds a table explaining which type of bands she should use based on her weight and the number of unassisted pull ups she can do.

The table is shown below.

	Body Weight (pounds)					
Unassisted pull ups	*90–120*	*121–150*	*151–200*	*201–250*	*251–300*	*300+*
0–4	D	D and A	E	F	F	G and A
5–8	C and A	D	E	E	E and B	G
9–11	C	D	D and C	E	E and A	F
12–15	C	C and B	D and B	D and C	E	E and C
16–20	B	C	D	D and B	E	E

Jane weighs herself. She is 10 stone and 1 pound.

1 stone = 14 pounds

Jane can do 3 unassisted pull ups.

(a) Which band(s) does the table recommend that Jane should buy? **1**

MARKS | DO NOT WRITE IN THIS MARGIN

5. (continued)

Jane's personal trainer, Lynn, wants to buy one of each band A to G.

The recommended retail prices (RRP) of the bands are shown in the table below.

Band	Colour	RRP
A	Yellow	£2·50
B	Red	£3·90
C	Black	£8·95
D	Purple	£10·95
E	Green	£14·00
F	Blue	£17·00
G	Orange	£18·50

To buy all of the bands individually, the total RRP would be £75·80.

Lynn considers the following special offers.

Shop 1

Shop 2

Shop 3

(b) Which shop offers the cheapest option for buying one of each band? **3**

Use your working to justify your answer.

MARKS DO NOT WRITE IN THIS MARGIN

6. The mathematics teachers in a school win a lottery.

They decide to share their winnings **in proportion to** the amount they each pay per week.

They each pay the following amounts per week:

Mr Jones	£0·50
Miss Smith	£2·00
Mr Ross	£2·50
Mr Young	£4·00

Mr Young's share is £2 794 000.

Calculate how much the teachers win in total. **3**

MARKS DO NOT WRITE IN THIS MARGIN

7. Aneesa makes enamelled badges.

Each badge is made from metal.

The shape of the badge is shown below.

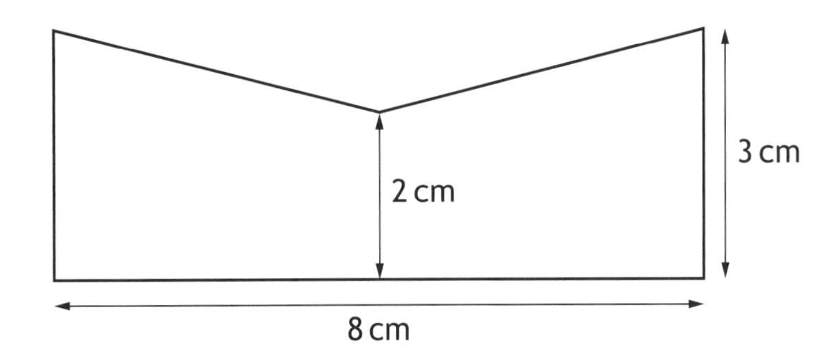

(a) Calculate the area of the front of each badge. **2**

The front of each badge is covered with enamel.

The enamel that Aneesa buys costs £90 for one pack.

One pack will cover 180 cm^2.

She makes as many badges as possible from one pack.

The metal that she uses costs £3 for each badge.

To make a profit, Aneesa adds an extra £17 to the cost of each badge.

(b) Calculate her selling price for each badge. **3**

DO NOT WRITE IN THIS MARGIN

8. Natalie is donating blood.

Whilst donating blood she notices a chart.

The chart states that not every blood type can be given to every patient.

The table shows which patients each blood type can help.

Blood type can be either positive (+) or negative (–).

Donor's Blood Type

Patient's Blood Type	O–	O+	B–	B+	A–	A+	AB–	AB+
AB+	✓	✓	✓	✓	✓	✓	✓	✓
AB–	✓		✓		✓		✓	
A+	✓	✓			✓	✓		
A–	✓				✓			
B+	✓	✓	✓	✓				
B–	✓		✓					
O+	✓	✓						
O–	✓							

For example the blood of a donor with blood type AB– can only be given safely to a patient with blood type AB+ or AB–.

Natalie then notices a graph showing the blood type of a random sample of **100** people in Scotland.

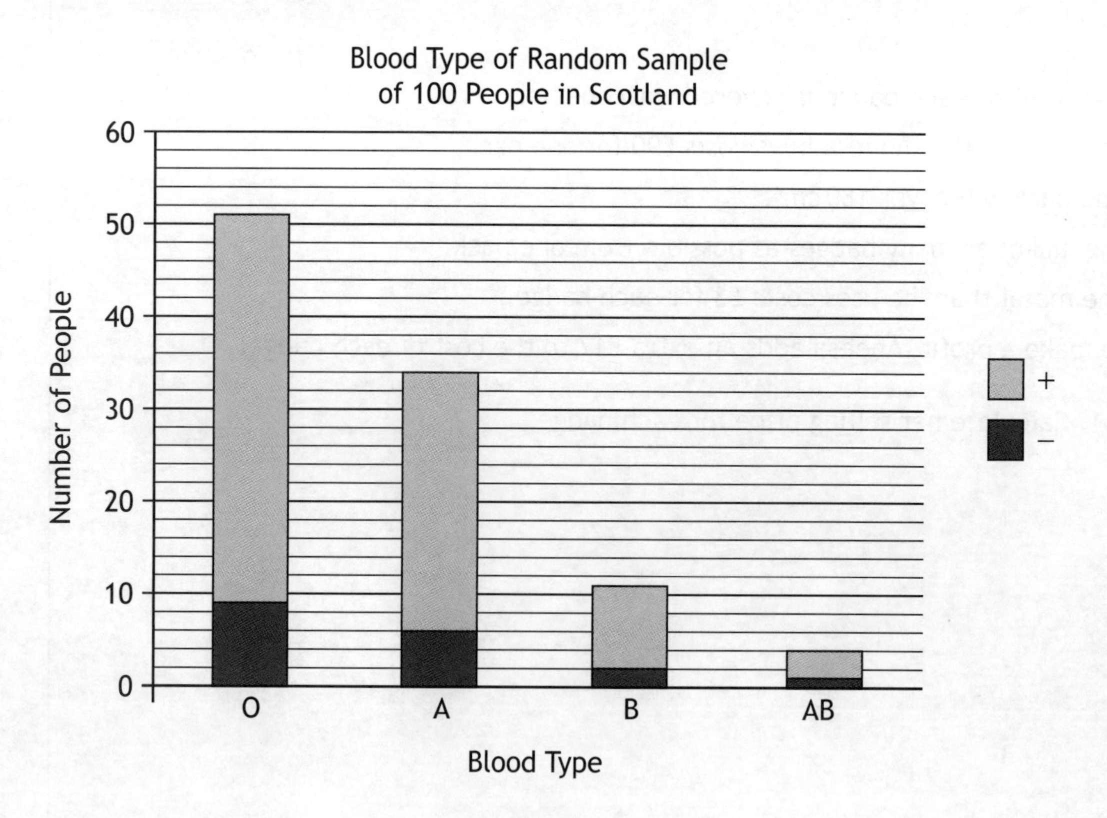

MARKS DO NOT WRITE IN THIS MARGIN

8. (continued)

Natalie's blood type is B+.

What fraction of the people sampled could safely be given Natalie's blood? 3

MARKS | DO NOT WRITE IN THIS MARGIN

9. A new design is discussed for a glue dispenser.

It is to be made from two plates of plastic.

Each plate is in the shape of a right angled triangle and a semi-circle as shown.

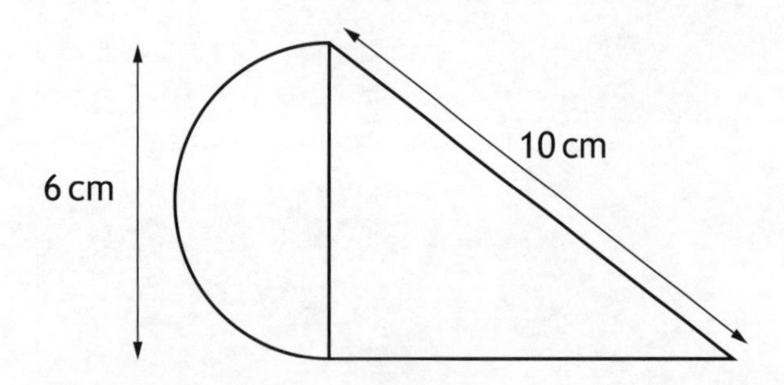

(a) Calculate the perimeter of each plate. **4**

Use $\pi = 3{\cdot}14$.

MARKS | DO NOT WRITE IN THIS MARGIN

9. (continued)

A rectangular piece of plastic 0·5 cm wide is bent and wrapped around the perimeter of the two plates to join them together.

The rectangular piece of plastic will be 0·3 cm shorter than the perimeter of the shape to allow the glue to flow.

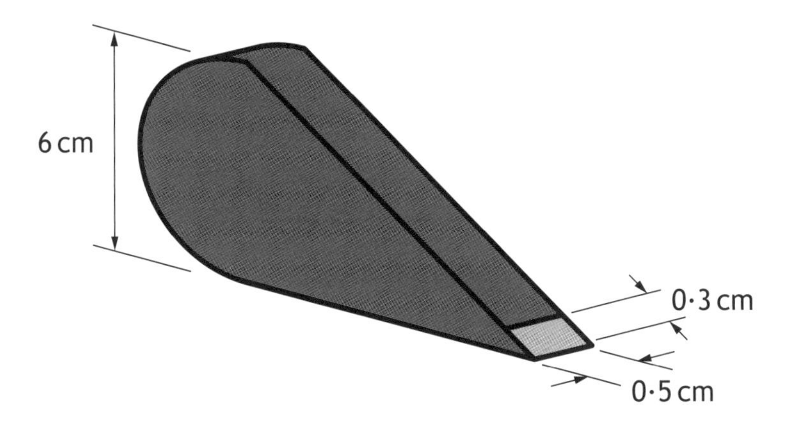

(b) Calculate the area of the **rectangular** piece of plastic required to hold the plates together. **2**

[END OF QUESTION PAPER]

MARKS | DO NOT WRITE IN THIS MARGIN

ADDITIONAL SPACE FOR ANSWERS

Additional grid for Question 3 (a)

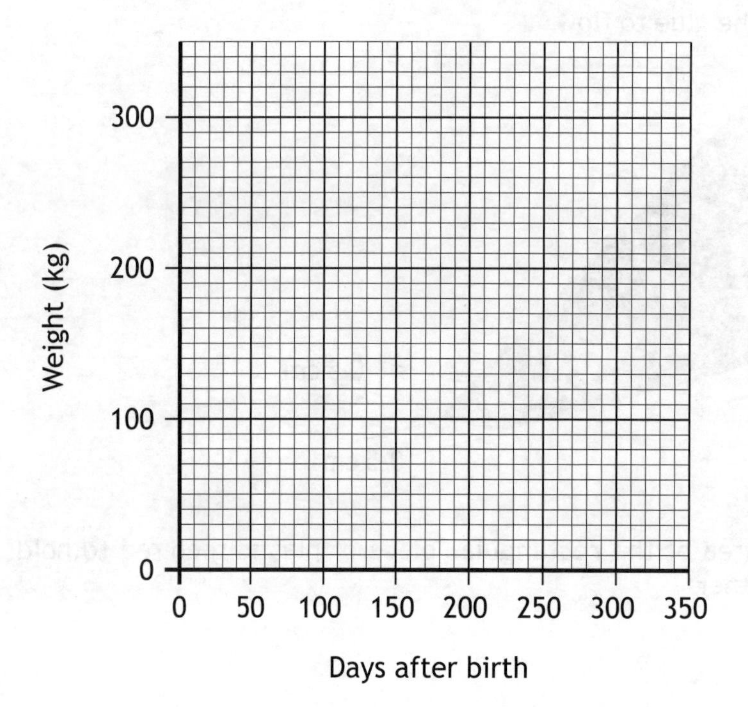

MARKS | DO NOT WRITE IN THIS MARGIN

ADDITIONAL SPACE FOR ANSWERS

MARKS DO NOT WRITE IN THIS MARGIN

ADDITIONAL SPACE FOR ANSWERS

FOR OFFICIAL USE

N5

National
Qualifications
2017

Mark

X744/75/02

Lifeskills Mathematics
Paper 2

MONDAY, 29 MAY

2:10 PM – 3:50 PM

Fill in these boxes and read what is printed below.

Full name of centre

Town

Forename(s)

Surname

Number of seat

Date of birth

Day Month Year

Scottish candidate number

Total marks — 55

Attempt ALL questions.

You may use a calculator.

Full credit will be given only to solutions which contain appropriate working.

State the units for your answer where appropriate.

Write your answers clearly in the spaces provided in this booklet. Additional space for answers is provided at the end of this booklet. If you use this space you must clearly identify the question number you are attempting.

Use **blue** or **black** ink.

Before leaving the examination room you must give this book to the Invigilator; if you do not, you may lose all the marks for this paper.

FORMULAE LIST

Circumference of a circle: $C = \pi d$

Area of a circle: $A = \pi r^2$

Theorem of Pythagoras:

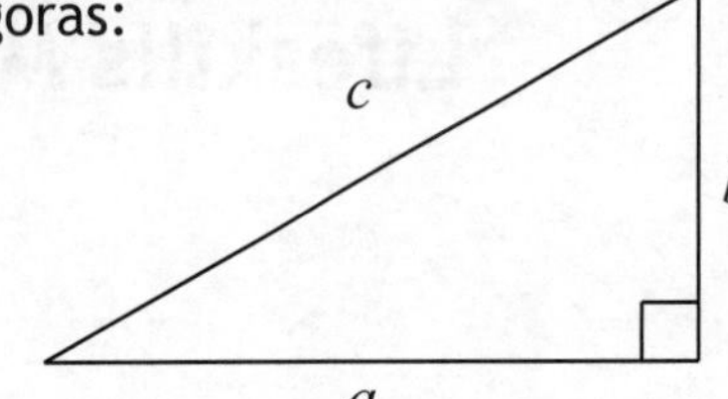

$a^2 \quad b^2 \quad c^2$

Volume of a cylinder: $V = \pi r^2 h$

Volume of a prism: $V = Ah$

Volume of a cone: $V = \frac{1}{3}\pi r^2 h$

Volume of a sphere: $V = \frac{4}{3}\pi r^3$

Standard deviation: $s = \sqrt{\frac{\Sigma(x-\overline{x})^2}{n-1}} = \sqrt{\frac{\Sigma x^2 - (\Sigma x)^2/n}{n-1}}$, where n is the sample size.

Gradient:

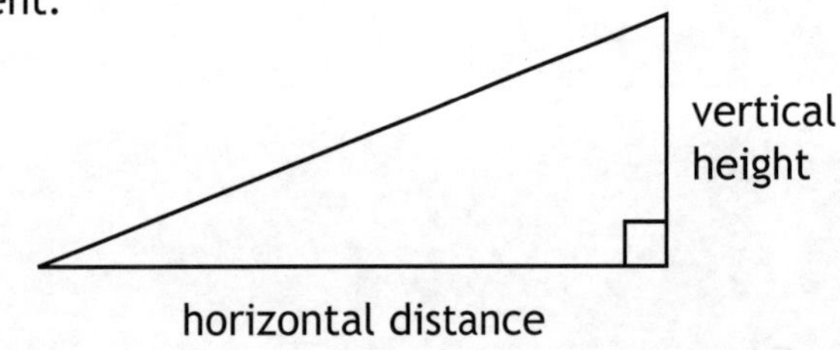

$$\text{gradient} = \frac{\text{vertical height}}{\text{horizontal distance}}$$

MARKS DO NOT WRITE IN THIS MARGIN

Total marks — 55

Attempt ALL questions

1. The Victorians used stoneware hot water bottles.

   They were semi-circular prisms as shown.

   The diameter of the bottle is 14 cm and the length is 30 cm.

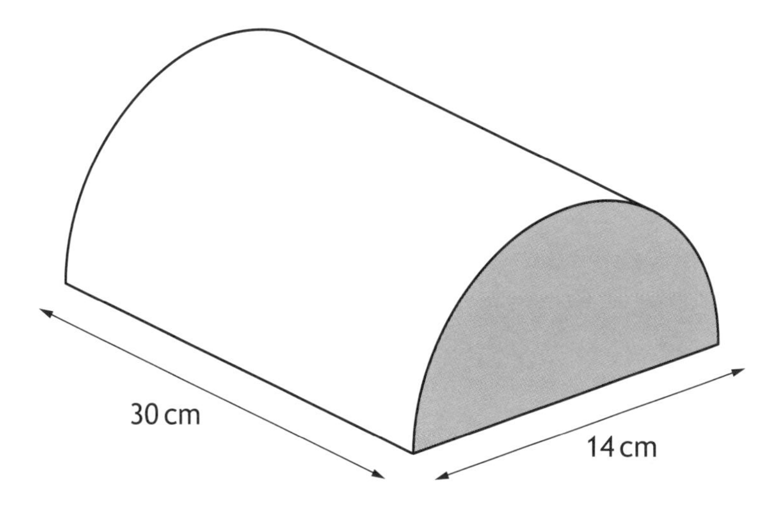

   Calculate the volume of the hot water bottle. **3**

MARKS | DO NOT WRITE IN THIS MARGIN

2. Asif bought 8000 shares in a local company in April 2013.

Each share cost him 73 pence.

The value of the shares

- decreased by 3% in the first year then,
- increased by 4·2% in each of the next **two years**.

(a) How much were Asif's shares worth in total in April 2016? **5**

In April 2017 Asif's shares were worth £6560 in total.

He decided to sell 5000 of his shares.

He was charged £12·95 commission on his sale.

(b) How much did he receive from the sale of the shares? **2**

MARKS DO NOT WRITE IN THIS MARGIN

3. Kyle is buying a new three piece suite.

It is advertised at a price of £1260.

Kyle can't afford to pay this all at once.

He decides to use a payment plan to buy the three piece suite.

The **total price** of the payment plan is **12% more** than the advertised price.

The payments are calculated as follows:

- deposit of $\frac{1}{3}$ of the total price
- 8 equal monthly instalments
- final payment of £200.

How much will each monthly instalment be? 4

MARKS | DO NOT WRITE IN THIS MARGIN

4. The back to back stem and leaf diagram shows data gathered at a gymnasium before and after walking on a treadmill.

Heart rate data (beats per minute (bpm))

Before		**After**
9 8 3 2 0	5	9
6 6 6 1 1 0 0	6	2 4 7 8 8
9 6 2	7	1 1 1 8
	8	2 4 9
	9	2 5
n = 15		n = 15

7 | 8 = 78

(a) State the most common heart rate (bpm) **after** walking on the treadmill. **1**

(b) What is the difference in the median heart rates (bpm) before and after walking on the treadmill? **2**

MARKS DO NOT WRITE IN THIS MARGIN

4. **(continued)**

(c) Construct a boxplot to show the heart rate data **after** exercise. 4

(An additional diagram, if required, can be found on *Page sixteen*.)

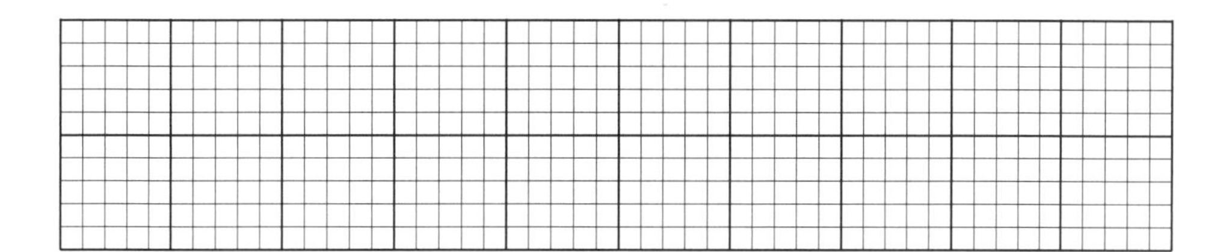

MARKS | DO NOT WRITE IN THIS MARGIN

5. Mr and Mrs Sibbald went on a cruise.

Part of the cruise involved sailing from Villefranche to Livorno.

The map below shows the route the ship takes.

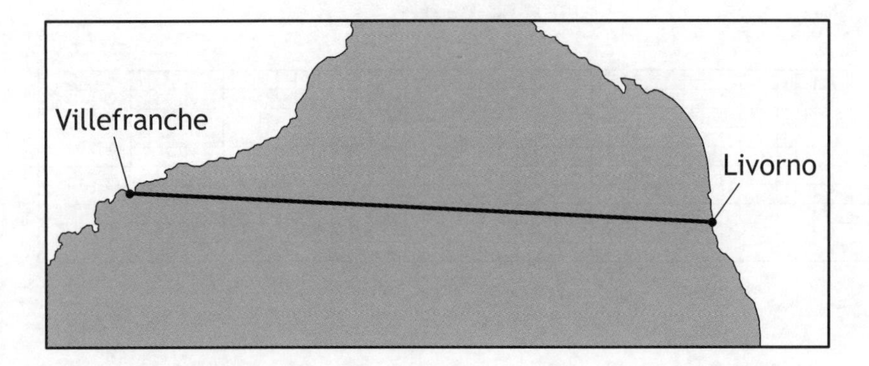

The scale of the map is 1 : 3 000 000

(a) Calculate the distance from Villefranche to Livorno. **2**

Give your answer in kilometres.

It took 7 hours and 30 minutes to sail from Villefranche to Livorno.

(b) Calculate the average speed of the ship's journey. **3**

Give your answer in knots.

1 kilometre per hour = 0·54 knots

Round your answer to 2 significant figures.

MARKS | DO NOT WRITE IN THIS MARGIN

5. (continued)

Mr and Mrs Sibbald took £2400 spending money.

They exchanged 55% of their money into euro, to spend ashore.

The exchange rate was **£1 = 1·15 euro.**

By the end of the cruise they had spent 1379 euro.

(c) Calculate how many euro they had left at the end of the cruise. **2**

Mr and Mrs Sibbald take part in an on board lottery which consists of a draw from a set of 32 balls numbered from 1 to 32.

(d) (i) What is the probability that the first ball drawn has a number greater than 25? **1**

In the draw four numbered balls are drawn and not replaced.

A further bonus ball is also drawn.

(ii) What is the probability of the number 9 being drawn as the bonus ball if it was not drawn in the first four? **2**

MARKS | DO NOT WRITE IN THIS MARGIN

6. Russell is a lorry driver for a mail delivery company.

The mail is packed into cages which are then loaded on to the lorry.

His lorry has two levels for fitting cages.

Each cage has wheels on the bottom and must always be **loaded upright**.

The dimensions of the cage and the internal dimensions of the back of the lorry are shown in the diagrams.

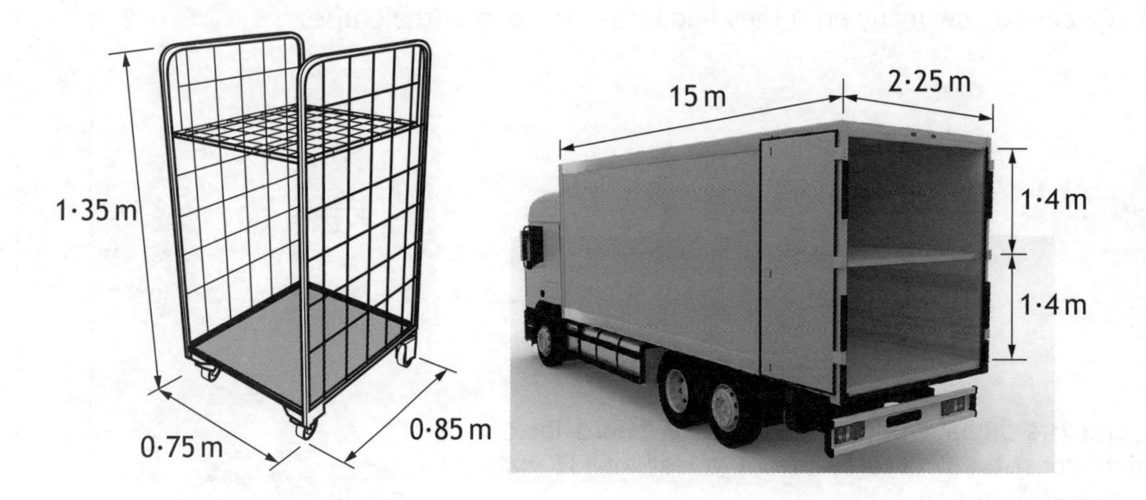

(a) What is the maximum number of cages that can be loaded into the back of the lorry? **3**

MARKS | DO NOT WRITE IN THIS MARGIN

6. (continued)

Russell works night shift.

- He works from 2300 until 0900 the next day.
- His rate of pay is £14·40 per hour.
- He gets paid time and a half between 2200 and 0730.
- He works 5 shifts each week.

(b) Calculate his weekly gross pay. **3**

MARKS DO NOT WRITE IN THIS MARGIN

7. Mr Mackenzie has decided to move to South Africa with his family. He has been offered jobs in both Durban and Cape Town.

The typical monthly temperatures from March to August in Durban are recorded in the table below.

Month	**Temperature** (°C)
March	24
April	22
May	19
June	18
July	17
August	17

(a) For the typical monthly temperatures in Durban, calculate:

(i) the mean; **1**

(ii) the standard deviation. **3**

MARKS | DO NOT WRITE IN THIS MARGIN

7. (continued)

In Cape Town the mean monthly temperature for the same period is 15·5 °C and the standard deviation is 1·87 °C.

(b) Make two valid comments comparing the temperatures in both cities. **2**

Mr Mackenzie accepts the job in Durban.

As part of his job he is in contact with the London, New York and Mumbai offices of the company he works for.

He is planning a conference call at 3:30 pm the following day, from his office in Durban.

At 17:25 he noticed the clocks on the wall of his office showed the times below.

10:25	15:25	17:25	22:55
New York	London	Durban	Mumbai

All offices work 08:00 to 18:00 local time.

(c) Which offices are available to take part in the conference call? **3**

MARKS DO NOT WRITE IN THIS MARGIN

8. Zuzanna is remodelling her shower room.

She considers two designs.

The first design has a pentagonal shower tray.

The door will be fitted on the side of the tray as shown.

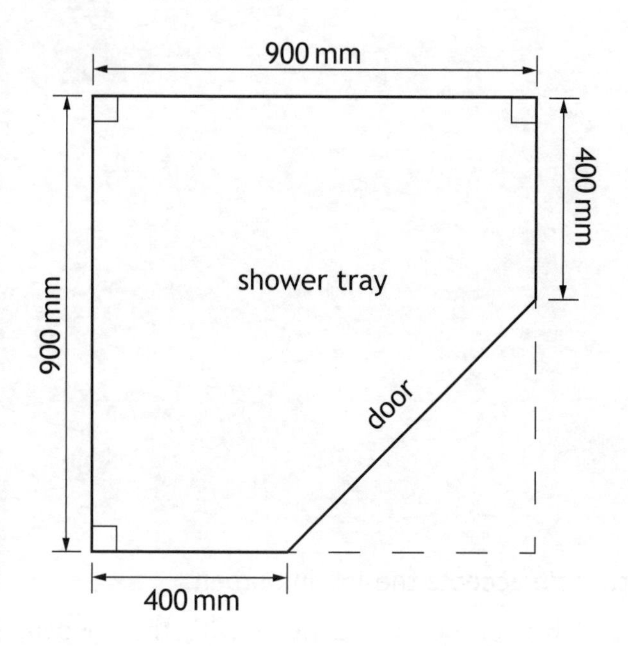

(a) Calculate the length of the side where the door will go. **3**

(b) Calculate the area of the pentagonal shower tray. **2**

MARKS DO NOT WRITE IN THIS MARGIN

8. (continued)

The second design that Zuzanna is considering is the offset quadrant shower tray shown below.

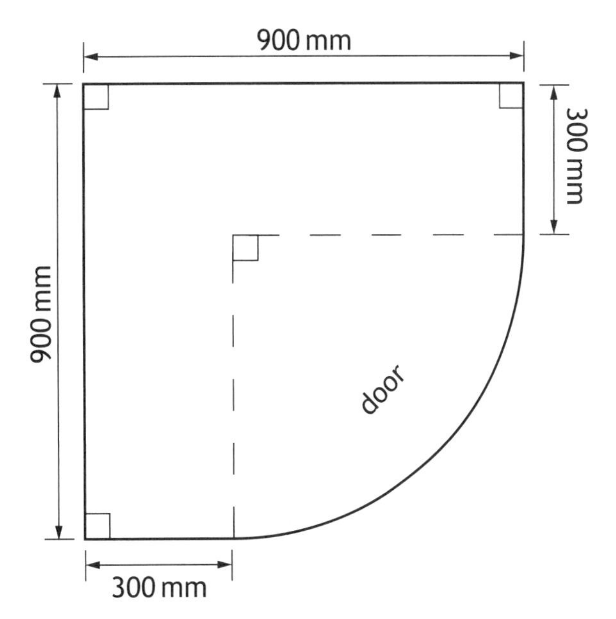

The offset quadrant design has quarter of a circle forming part of the edge.

(c) Zuzanna will choose the design that gives the greater area.

Which design will Zuzanna choose, the pentagonal or the offset quadrant shower tray? 4

Use your working to justify your answer.

[END OF QUESTION PAPER]

MARKS DO NOT WRITE IN THIS MARGIN

ADDITIONAL SPACE FOR ANSWERS

Additional diagram for use in Question 4 (c).

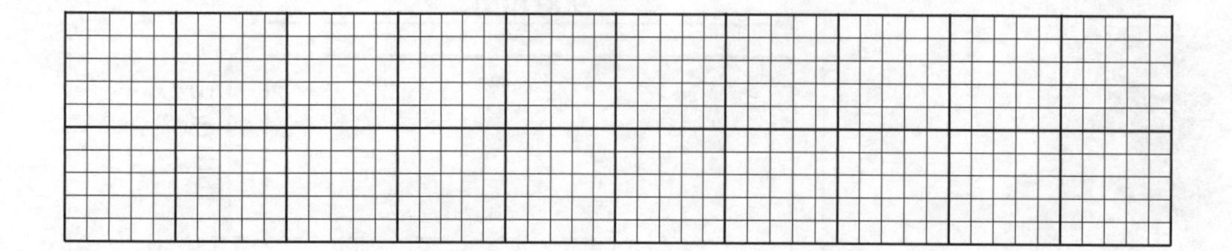

MARKS | DO NOT WRITE IN THIS MARGIN

ADDITIONAL SPACE FOR ANSWERS

MARKS DO NOT WRITE IN THIS MARGIN

ADDITIONAL SPACE FOR ANSWERS

MARKS | DO NOT WRITE IN THIS MARGIN

ADDITIONAL SPACE FOR ANSWERS

MARKS | DO NOT WRITE IN THIS MARGIN

ADDITIONAL SPACE FOR ANSWERS

NATIONAL 5

2017 Specimen Question Paper

FOR OFFICIAL USE

N5 National Qualifications SPECIMEN ONLY

Mark

S844/75/01

Applications of Mathematics Paper 1 (Non-Calculator)

Date — Not applicable

Duration — 1 hour 5 minutes

Fill in these boxes and read what is printed below.

Full name of centre

Town

Forename(s)

Surname

Number of seat

Date of birth

Day Month Year

Scottish candidate number

Total marks — 45

Attempt ALL questions.

You may NOT use a calculator.

To earn full marks you must show your working in your answers.

State the units for your answer where appropriate.

Write your answers clearly in the spaces provided in this booklet. Additional space for answers is provided at the end of this booklet. If you use this space you must clearly identify the question number you are attempting.

Use **blue** or **black** ink.

Before leaving the examination room you must give this booklet to the Invigilator; if you do not, you may lose all the marks for this paper.

FORMULAE LIST

Circumference of a circle: $C = \pi d$

Area of a circle: $A = \pi r^2$

Theorem of Pythagoras:

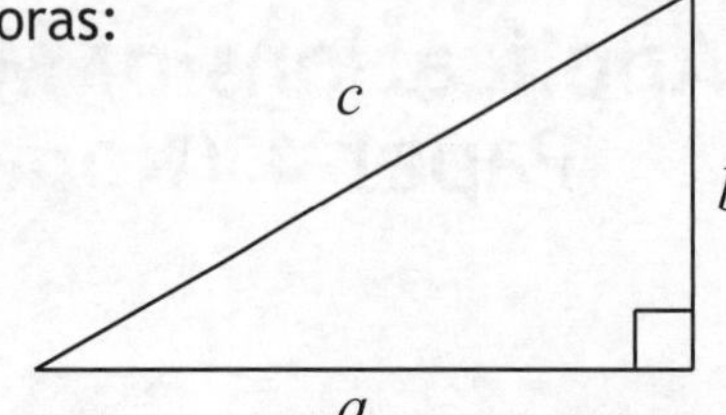

$a^2 \quad b^2 \quad c^2$

Volume of a cylinder: $V = \pi r^2 h$

Volume of a prism: $V = Ah$

Volume of a cone: $V = \frac{1}{3}\pi r^2 h$

Volume of a sphere: $V = \frac{4}{3}\pi r^3$

Standard deviation: $s = \sqrt{\frac{\Sigma(x-\overline{x})^2}{n-1}} = \sqrt{\frac{\Sigma x^2 - (\Sigma x)^2/n}{n-1}}$, where n is the sample size.

Gradient:

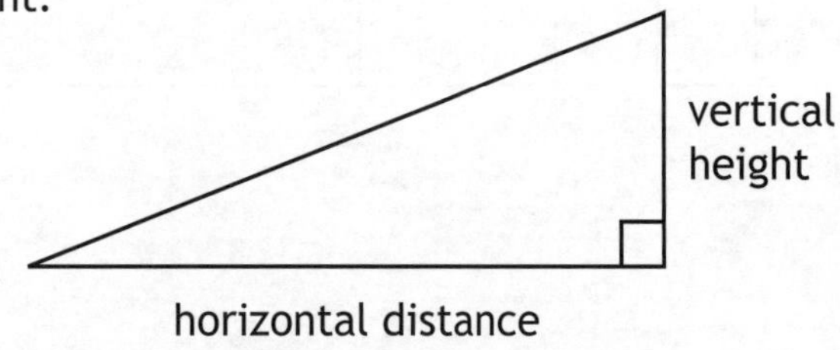

$$\text{gradient} = \frac{\text{vertical height}}{\text{horizontal distance}}$$

MARKS | DO NOT WRITE IN THIS MARGIN

Total marks — 45

Attempt ALL questions

1. Liam is on holiday in New York.

He looks at the world time app on his phone.

The display shows the times below:

His flight to Glasgow departs New York at 8:00 am local time.

The flight time is 6 hours 30 minutes.

Calculate the local time when the plane lands in Glasgow. **2**

MARKS | DO NOT WRITE IN THIS MARGIN

2. S6 pupils were asked to choose their favourite subject.

The results are shown in the table below.

Subject	Boys	Girls
Geography	11	7
French	9	14
Maths	18	13
Spanish	10	12
Modern Studies	18	8
Total	66	54

Calculate the probability that a boy from this group chose French as his favourite subject.

Give your answer as a fraction in its simplest form. 2

3. A company orders a bag of washers with a thickness of $2{\cdot}4 \pm 0{\cdot}05$ mm.

An inspector takes a sample from the bag of washers.

The thicknesses, in mm, of the washers in this sample are shown below.

2·44, 2·37, 2·36, 2·45, 2·35

2·35, 2·44, 2·43, 2·34, 2·40

2·40, 2·41, 2·39, 2·38, 2·46

2·41, 2·39, 2·53, 2·36, 2·37

For the bag to be accepted, at least 88% of the washers in this sample must be within tolerance.

Will the bag be accepted? 3

MARKS | DO NOT WRITE IN THIS MARGIN

4. The table below shows the vehicle tax to be paid on different vehicles.

The amount of vehicle tax paid depends on the CO_2 emissions of the vehicle and the fuel type.

		Tax for Petrol and Diesel Cars				
		Non Direct Debit		Direct Debit		
Bands	CO_2 emission figure (g/km)	12 months	Six months	Single 12 month payment	Total payable by 12 monthly instalments	Single six month payment
Band A	Up to 100	£0	–	–	–	–
Band B	101 to 110	£20	–	£20	£21	–
Band C	111 to 120	£30	–	£30	£31·50	–
Band D	121 to 130	£110	£60·50	£110	£115·50	£57·75
Band E	131 to 140	£130	£71·50	£130	£136·50	£68·25
Band F	141 to 150	£145	£79·75	£145	£152·25	£76·13
Band G	151 to 165	£180	£99	£180	£189	£94·50
Band H	166 to 175	£205	£112·75	£205	£215·25	£107·63
Band I	176 to 185	£225	£123·75	£225	£236·25	£118·13
Band J	186 to 200	£265	£145·75	£265	£278·25	£139·13
Band K	201 to 225	£290	£159·50	£290	£304·50	£152·25
Band L	226 to 255	£490	£269·50	£490	£514·50	£257·25
Band M	Over 255	£505	£277·75	£505	£530·25	£265·13

Tom buys a petrol car which has a CO_2 emission figure of 142 g/km.

Tom decides to pay his vehicle tax by direct debit in two single six month payments.

How much more expensive is this than a single 12 month payment by direct debit? **3**

MARKS | DO NOT WRITE IN THIS MARGIN

5. This back-to-back stem and leaf diagram represents the number of hours a class spends on social networking websites in a week.

Girls		Boys
	0	3 6 8 9
8 4 3 0	1	1 2 4 7 7 8 9
9 8 7 6 2 2 1	2	2 6 7 8 8
7 2 0	3	
2	4	

n = 15   n = 16

KEY

3 | 1 | represents 13 hours

| 2 | 5 represents 25 hours

(a) A boxplot is drawn to represent one set of data.

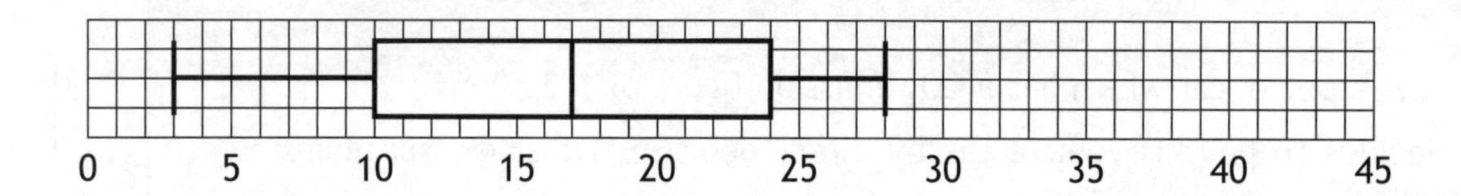

Which set of data does this represent?

Give a reason for your answer. **1**

(b) For the other set of data, state:

the median

the lower quartile

the upper quartile. **2**

MARKS DO NOT WRITE IN THIS MARGIN

5. (continued)

(c) Construct a box plot for the second set of data. 2

(An additional diagram, if required, can be found on *Page sixteen*.)

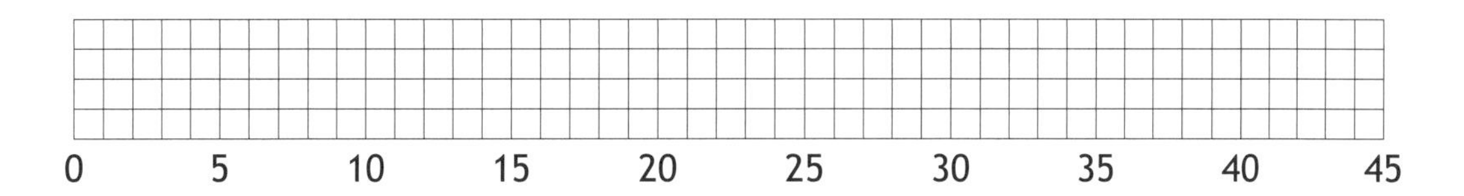

6. Mo is an electrician.

The table below shows the hours that Mo worked last week.

Monday	09:00 to 12:30	13:30 to 18:00	
Tuesday	09:00 to 12:30	13:30 to 18:00	
Wednesday	09:00 to 12:30	13:30 to 18:00	18:30 to 21:30
Thursday	09:00 to 12:30	13:30 to 18:00	18:30 to 21:30
Friday	09:00 to 12:30	13:30 to 18:00	

His basic hourly rate is £15·60.

Hours worked between 6 pm and 7 am are paid at time and a half.

Calculate his gross pay for last week. 3

MARKS | DO NOT WRITE IN THIS MARGIN

7. Jack is going to a festival in the Czech Republic from his home in Glasgow.

His mum orders the tickets costing 1500 Czech Koruna.

His mum lives in Poland so he must pay her back in Polish Zloty.

Rates of exchange	
Pounds Sterling (£)	**Other Currencies**
1	30·00 Czech Koruna
1	4·96 Polish Zloty

Calculate how many Polish Zloty he must give to his mum. **2**

MARKS DO NOT WRITE IN THIS MARGIN

8. A class of pupils were asked about how they travelled to school on a particular day.

- $\frac{1}{6}$ of the pupils were driven to school in a car.
- $\frac{2}{5}$ of the pupils took the bus.
- The rest of the pupils walked to school.

Calculate the fraction of pupils who walked to school. **3**

9. It takes 5 bakers 3 hours to decorate a tray of cupcakes.

All the bakers work at the same rate.

Calculate the time taken for 4 bakers working at this rate to decorate the same number of cupcakes.

Give your answer in **hours and minutes.** **3**

MARKS DO NOT WRITE IN THIS MARGIN

10. Canoeists in Scotland use water level data to decide if there is enough water in a river to canoe down it.

The data for the River Tweed is shown below.

Table 1

Time	Water Level (metres)
Friday 2015	1·55
Friday 2200	1·58
Friday 2315	1·67
Saturday 0015	1·70
Saturday 0100	1·88
Saturday 0300	1·97
Saturday 0415	2·05

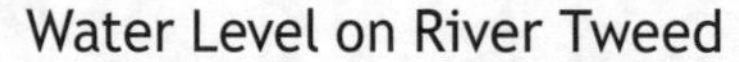

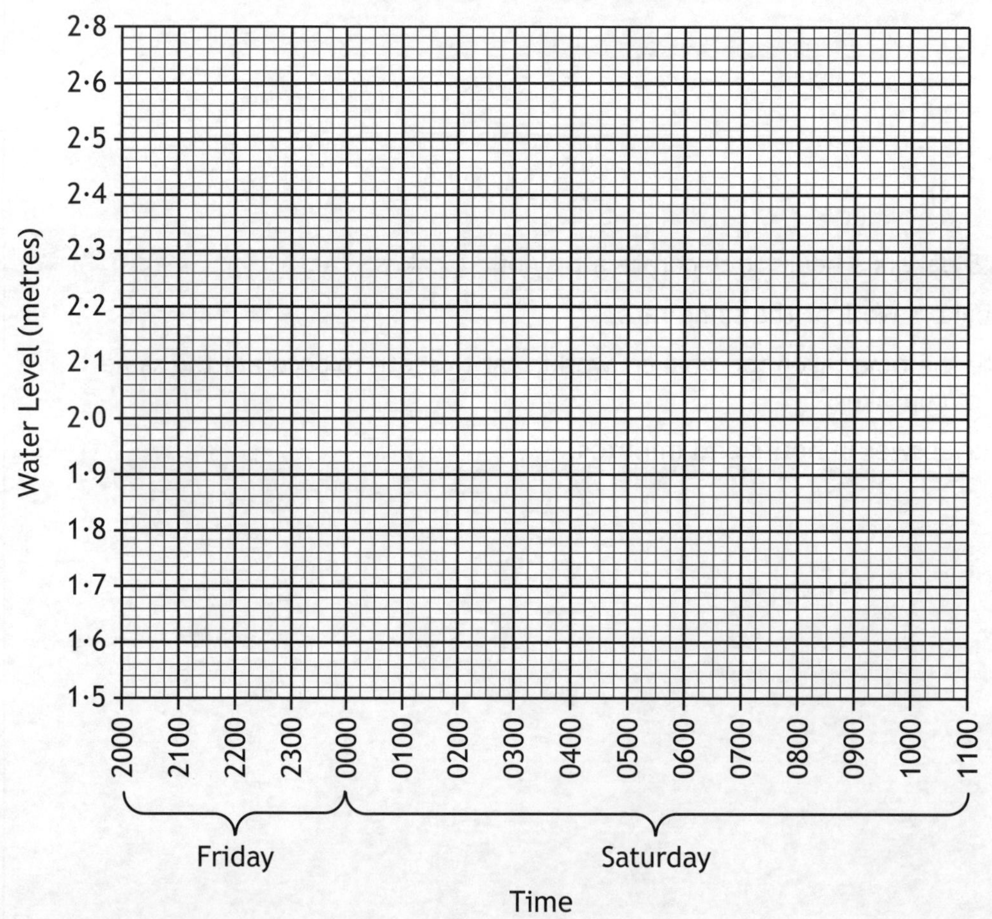

(a) (i) Plot the water levels on the scattergraph. **2**

(ii) Draw a line of best fit on the scattergraph. **1**

(An additional graph, if required, can be found on *Page sixteen*.)

MARKS | DO NOT WRITE IN THIS MARGIN

10. (continued)

(b) The water level is predicted to rise at the same rate until 1100 on Saturday.

The canoeists use their line of best fit to predict the water level of the River Tweed at 0830 on Saturday.

They hope that it will be "Very High".

Table 2

River Tweed	
Water level:	
Huge	> 3·5
Very High	2·5 - 3·5
High	2·0 - 2·5
Medium	1·7 - 2·0
Low	1·2 - 1·7
Scrapeable	0·0 - 1·2
Empty	never

Will the Tweed be "Very High" at 0830?

Justify your answer. **2**

MARKS | DO NOT WRITE IN THIS MARGIN

11. Mhairi bought 200 shares for £700.

She decides to sell them, but the share price has dropped to £2·75 per share.

She also has to pay a fee of 2½% of her selling price when she sells her shares.

Calculate the loss that she has made. **4**

MARKS | DO NOT WRITE IN THIS MARGIN

12. The diagram shows a planned zip line for a play park.

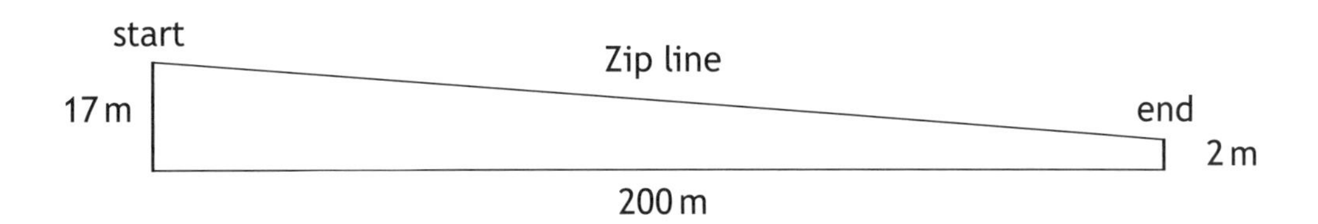

It is recommended that the average gradient of the zip line should be between 0·06 and 0·08 to be safe.

Does the planned zip line meet these safety recommendations?

Use your working to justify your answer. **3**

MARKS | DO NOT WRITE IN THIS MARGIN

13. Joe buys a plot of land in the shape of a rectangle and a semi-circle, as shown below.

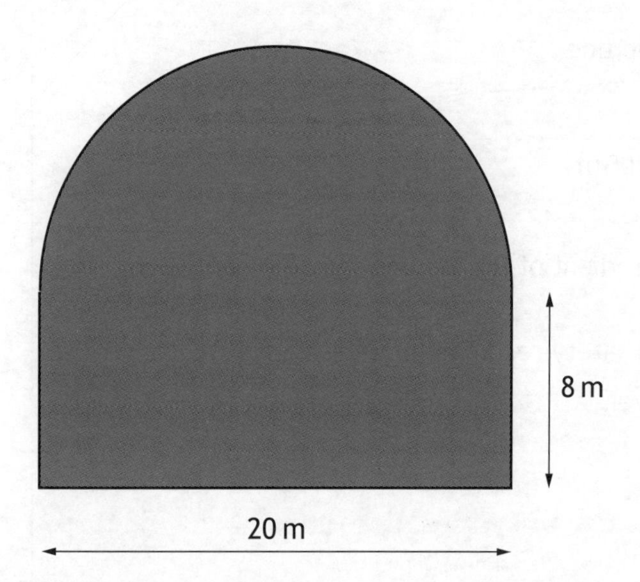

He plans to put a fence around the plot of land.

He employs Fence Direct to build the fence.

Fence Direct charges £15 per metre including all materials and labour.

(a) Calculate the cost of the fence. **3**

Take $\pi = 3{\cdot}14$.

MARKS DO NOT WRITE IN THIS MARGIN

13. (continued)

(b) Fence Direct provides a team of workers to build the fence.

The table shows the list of tasks and the time taken to complete them.

Task	Detail	Preceding Task	Time (hours)
A	Take down old fence	None	2
B	Measure length of fence needed	None	0·5
C	Mark on the ground where new posts must go	None	0·5
D	Collect materials and tools from yard	B	1
E	Hammer posts into the ground	A, C, D	4
F	Attach metal fencing to posts	E	2
G	Attach barbed wire to top of posts	F	1
H	Gather up rubbish	G	2
I	Gather up tools	G	0·5
J	Take rubbish to recycling centre	H	1
K	Put tools back in yard	I	0·5

Complete the diagram below by writing these tasks and times in the boxes. **2**

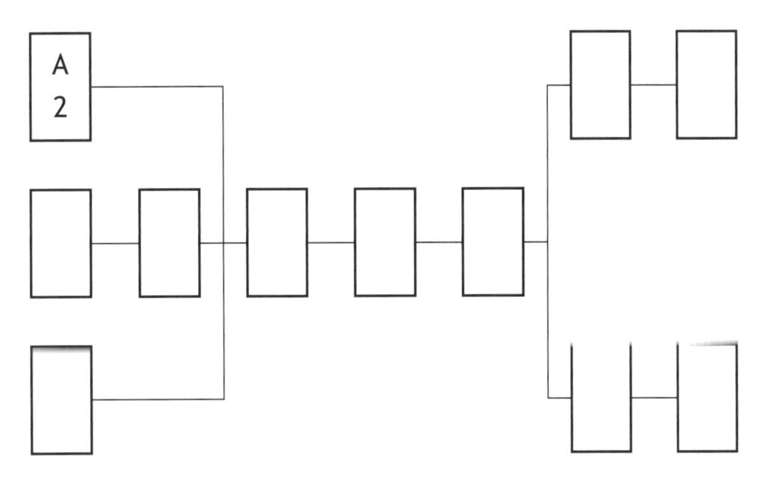

(An additional diagram, if required, can be found on *Page seventeen.*)

(c) Fence Direct claims that all of these tasks can be completed in 10 hours.

Is this a valid claim?

Use your working to justify your answer. **2**

[END OF SPECIMEN QUESTION PAPER]

MARKS | DO NOT WRITE IN THIS MARGIN

ADDITIONAL SPACE FOR ANSWERS

Additional diagram for Question 6 (c)

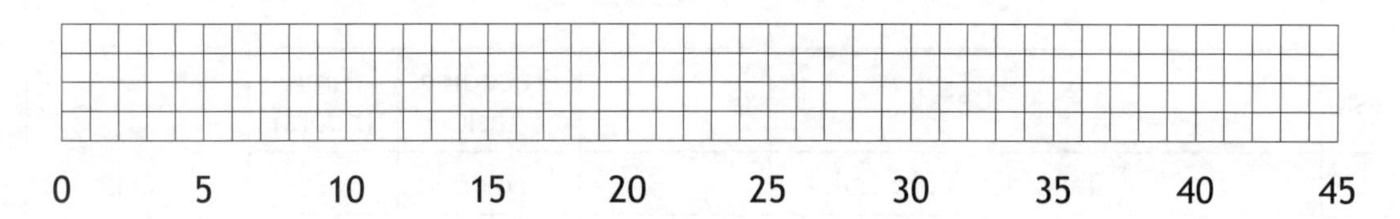

Additional graph for Question 10 (a)

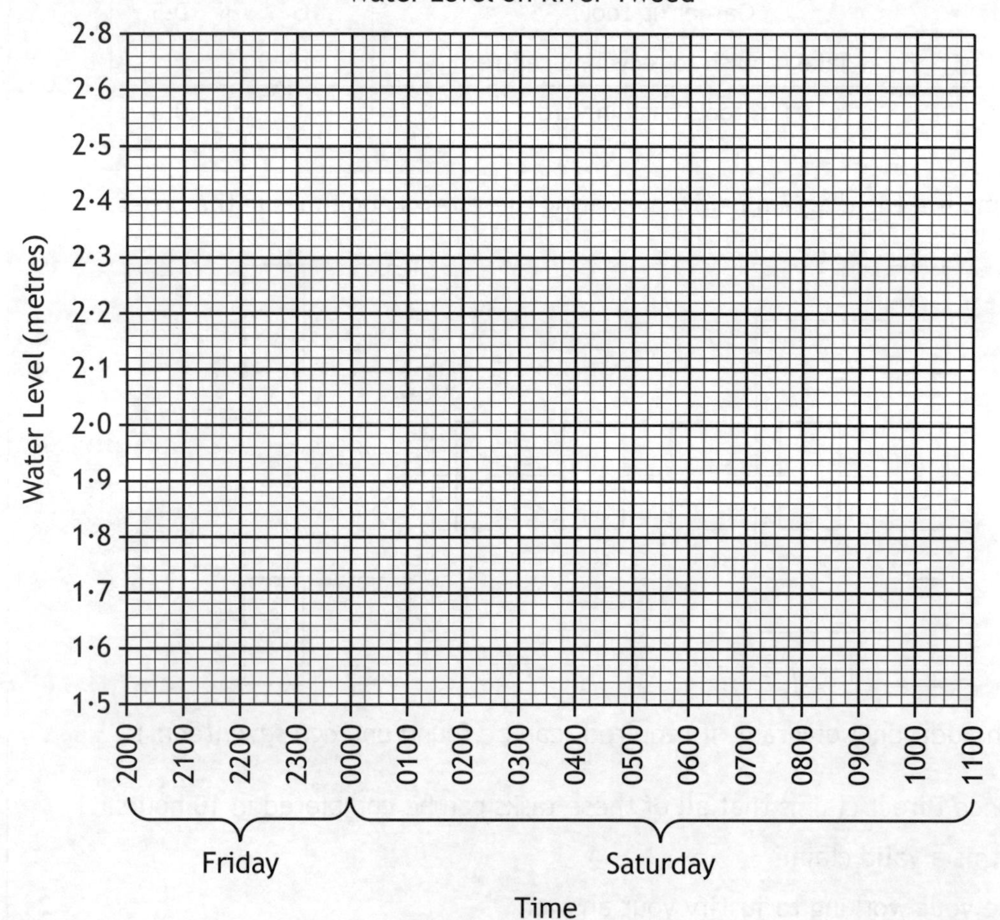

MARKS | DO NOT WRITE IN THIS MARGIN

ADDITIONAL SPACE FOR ANSWERS

Additional diagram for Question 13 (b)

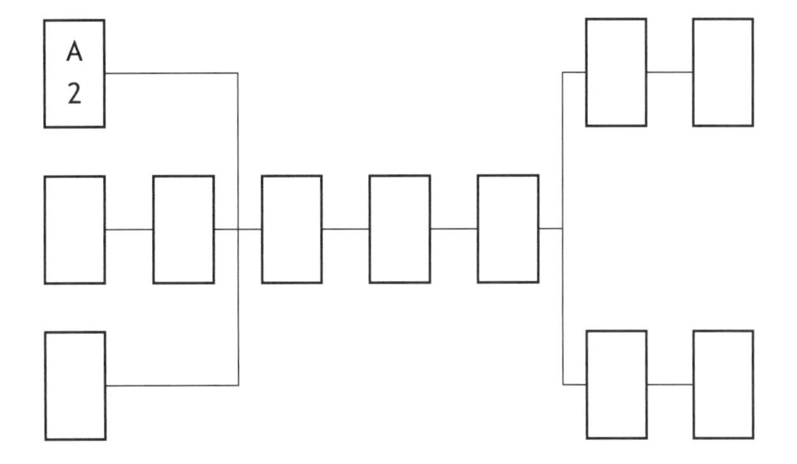

MARKS DO NOT WRITE IN THIS MARGIN

ADDITIONAL SPACE FOR ANSWERS

FOR OFFICIAL USE

N5

National Qualifications
SPECIMEN ONLY

Mark

S844/75/02

Applications of Mathematics
Paper 2

Date — Not applicable

Duration — 2 hours

Fill in these boxes and read what is printed below.

Full name of centre

Town

Forename(s)

Surname

Number of seat

Date of birth

Day Month Year

Scottish candidate number

Total marks — 65

Attempt ALL questions.

You may use a calculator.

To earn full marks you must show your working in your answers.

State the units for your answer where appropriate.

Write your answers clearly in the spaces provided in this booklet. Additional space for answers is provided at the end of this booklet. If you use this space you must clearly identify the question number you are attempting.

Use **blue** or **black** ink.

Before leaving the examination room you must give this booklet to the Invigilator; if you do not, you may lose all the marks for this paper.

FORMULAE LIST

Circumference of a circle: $C = \pi d$

Area of a circle: $A = \pi r^2$

Theorem of Pythagoras:

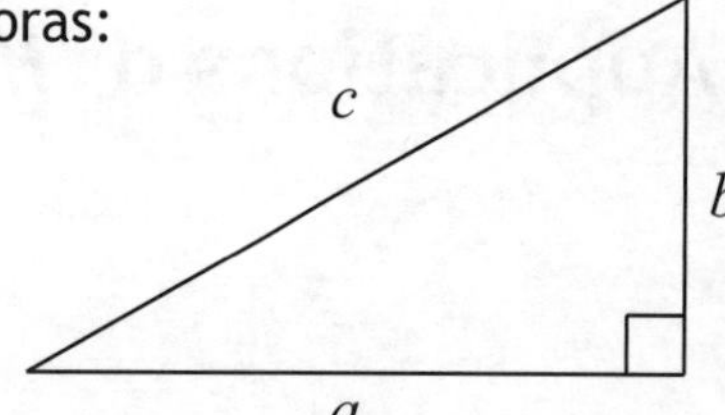

$a^2 \quad b^2 \quad c^2$

Volume of a cylinder: $V = \pi r^2 h$

Volume of a prism: $V = Ah$

Volume of a cone: $V = \frac{1}{3}\pi r^2 h$

Volume of a sphere: $V = \frac{4}{3}\pi r^3$

Standard deviation: $s = \sqrt{\frac{\Sigma(x - \overline{x})^2}{n-1}} = \sqrt{\frac{\Sigma x^2 - (\Sigma x)^2 / n}{n-1}}$, where n is the sample size.

Gradient:

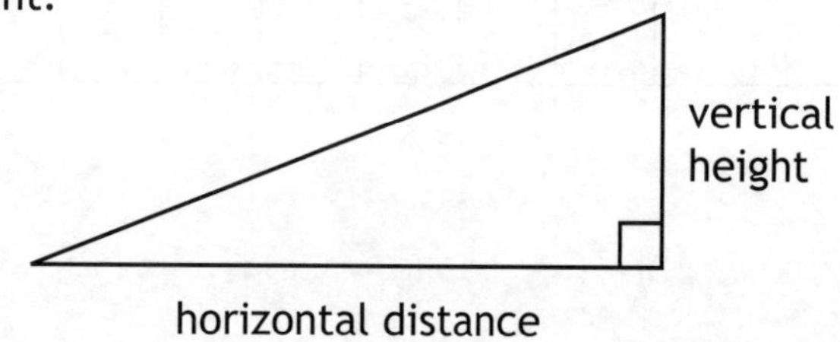

$$\text{gradient} = \frac{\text{vertical height}}{\text{horizontal distance}}$$

MARKS | DO NOT WRITE IN THIS MARGIN

Total marks — 65

Attempt ALL questions

1. Erin bought a yacht costing £780 000 in February 2013.

For the next three years the value of the yacht decreased by 4·1% per annum.

Calculate the value of the yacht in February 2016.

Give your answer to **3 significant figures**. 4

MARKS DO NOT WRITE IN THIS MARGIN

2. The fuel tank in Colin's car holds 64 litres of fuel.

Colin started with a full tank and used 40 litres of fuel.

Mark the amount of fuel **remaining** in the tank on the gauge shown below. 2

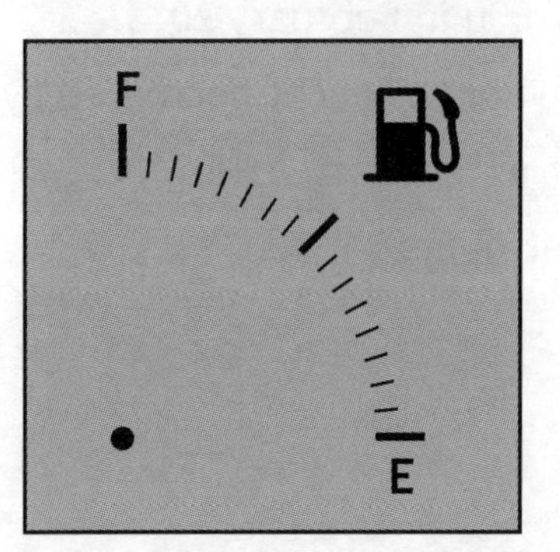

MARKS | DO NOT WRITE IN THIS MARGIN

3. An athlete without a coach runs a series of 400 metre races. A sample of his times, in seconds, is shown below.

47·8 48·3 50·2 49·5 46·9 49·5

(a) For these times, calculate:

(i) the mean; **1**

(ii) the standard deviation. **3**

(b) The same athlete then decides to train with a coach.

After training with the coach, the athlete runs a series of races which produces a mean of 49·3 seconds and a standard deviation of 0·23.

Make two valid comparisons about the times taken by the athlete before and after training with the coach. **2**

MARKS | DO NOT WRITE IN THIS MARGIN

4. A garage sells 150 cars in a month.

The bar chart below shows how many cars of each type are sold.

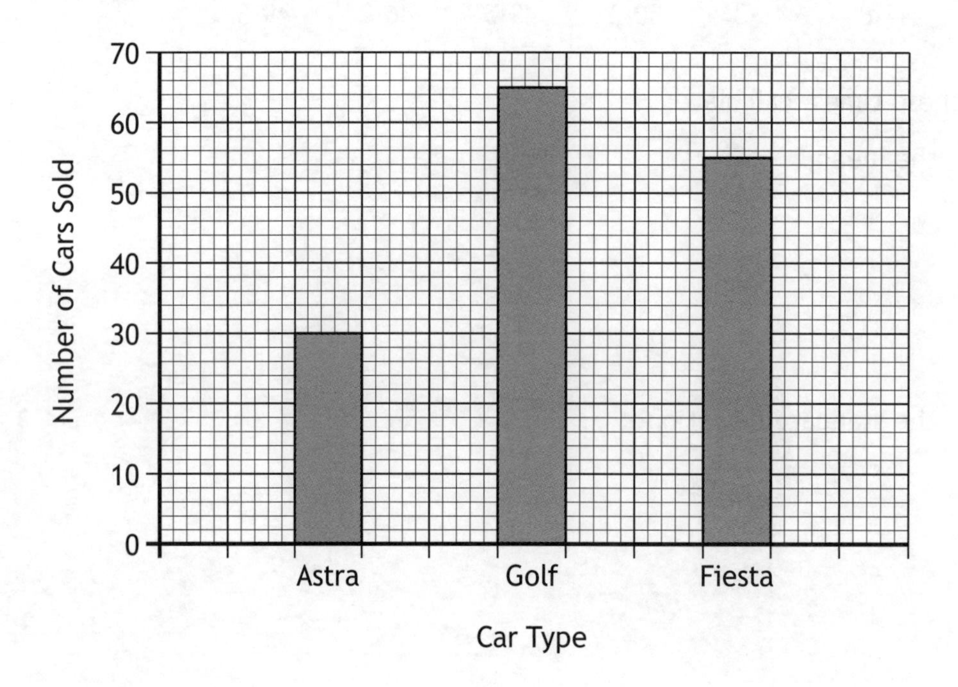

Construct a pie chart to show this information. **3**

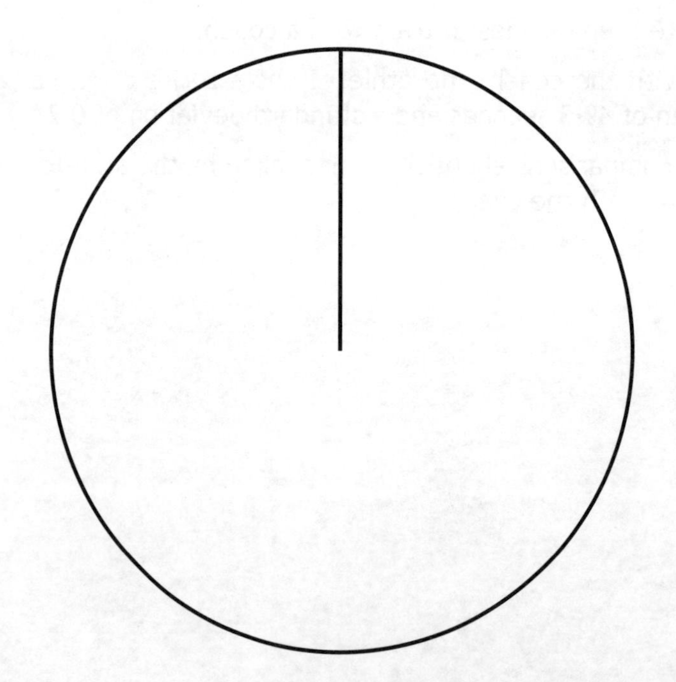

(An additional diagram, if required, can be found on *Page seventeen*.)

MARKS DO NOT WRITE IN THIS MARGIN

5. Donna makes tartan handbags.

She puts the bags into boxes. The boxes have the dimensions shown below.

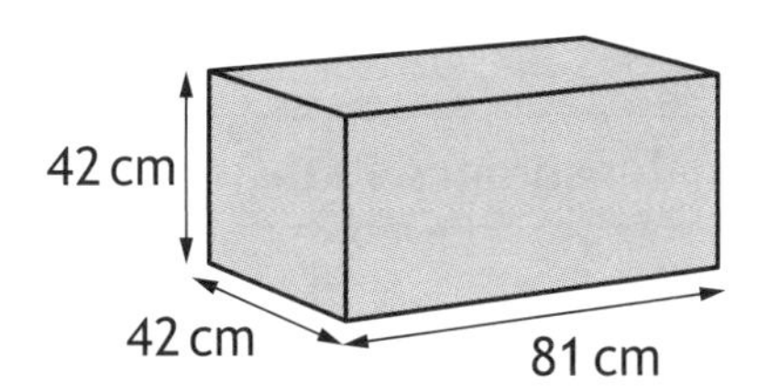

Donna exports her handbags to the USA in a container. The container has the internal dimensions shown below.

All the boxes must be aligned in the same direction.

(a) Calculate the maximum number of boxes that can fit in the container.

Use your working to justify your answer. **3**

(b) The rental and shipping of the container costs £1755.

Each box costs £2·99.

Each box holds 4 handbags.

Calculate the cost of shipping per handbag. **2**

MARKS | DO NOT WRITE IN THIS MARGIN

6. Graham earns £49 920 per annum.

National Insurance is calculated on a person's salary **before** deductions such as pension contributions.

National Insurance Rates	
Up to £8060	0%
From £8060 to £42 380	12%
Over £42 380	2%

(a) Calculate Graham's annual National Insurance payment. **3**

(b) Graham pays 9% of his annual salary into his pension.

Graham's annual income tax is £6870·04.

Graham is paid in 12 monthly payments.

Calculate Graham's monthly net pay. **3**

MARKS DO NOT WRITE IN THIS MARGIN

6. (continued)

(c) He wants to buy a new car.

The car loan and running costs would be £460 per month.

He makes a table to show his monthly income and outgoings.

	Income	**Outgoings**
Take home pay		
Rent		£750
Bills		£450
Food		£625
Entertainment		£125
Child care		£350

Will Graham have enough money each month to get this particular car?

Use your working to justify your answer. **2**

MARKS | DO NOT WRITE IN THIS MARGIN

7. The boat leaves from the harbour on a bearing of 045° for a distance of 22 miles to Puffin Island.

The boat leaves Puffin Island on a bearing of 170° and travels for a further 37 miles to Gull Isle.

(a) Construct a scale drawing to illustrate this journey.

Use a scale of 1 cm : 5 miles. **3**

(An additional diagram, if required, can be found on *Page eighteen*.)

The boat continues back to the harbour.

(b) Use the scale drawing to determine the bearing and distance of the harbour from the boat. **2**

MARKS | DO NOT WRITE IN THIS MARGIN

7. (continued)

(c) The boat leaves the harbour at 0930.

It stops for 1 hour 15 minutes at Puffin Island and 2 hours 50 minutes at Gull Isle.

The boat arrives back at the harbour at 1800 the same day.

Calculate the average speed of the boat whilst it is moving. **3**

MARKS | DO NOT WRITE IN THIS MARGIN

8. Fiona is planning to stay in New York, USA, for three days.
The table shows the attractions Fiona wants to visit and how much they cost.

Attraction	Full price in US Dollars
Empire State Building	\$32
Top of the Rock Observation Deck	\$30
Statue of Liberty Cruise	\$40
9/11 Memorial and Museum	\$24
Waxworks	\$37
One World Observatory	\$32

Fiona plans to buy a discount card to reduce the cost of visiting these attractions.

There are three different discount cards.

Not all of the attractions are included in all of the cards. Fiona must pay full price for these.

Card 1: NY Card

NY Card

Attractions:

★ Sea and Space Museum ★ ★ Top of the Rock Observation Deck ★
★ Museum of Natural History ★ ★ 9/11 Memorial and Museum ★
★ Statue of Liberty Cruise ★ ★ Empire State Building ★

★★★★ Total Cost \$114 ★★★★

Benefits:

These six attractions can be visited for a single payment of \$114.
This card can only be used once per attraction.
It is valid for 30 days from first use.

Card 2: Explore NY Card

Explore NY Card

Attractions:

9/11 Memorial and Museum • Statue of Liberty Cruise
Museum of Natural History • Sea and Space Museum
Empire State Building • Top of the Rock Observation Deck
Waxworks • Carnegie Hall • Rockefeller Centre Tour

Cost for any 3 attractions \$71

Benefits:

This card can be used for any 3 attractions from the list.
This card can only be used once per attraction.
It is valid for 30 days from first use.

MARKS | DO NOT WRITE IN THIS MARGIN

8. (continued)

Card 3: NY Town Pass

NY Town Pass

80+ attractions are included for one price.
The card is valid for 1, 2, 3 or 5 days.

Cost

$90	1 day pass	$180	3 day pass
$140	2 day pass	$190	5 day pass

Benefits:

All of Fiona's chosen attractions can be visited with this card.

(a) During her three-day visit, Fiona will visit two attractions each day.

Fiona is going to buy one discount card.

(i) Calculate the total cost of all six attractions if Fiona buys Card 1. **2**

(ii) Calculate the cheapest price that Fiona could pay for entry to her six chosen attractions. **4**

(b) Fiona pays the cheapest price for entry to her six chosen attractions.

She pays before leaving the UK.

The cost is £100·96.

Calculate the exchange rate that Fiona received.

Give your answer correct to **3 decimal places**. **2**

MARKS | DO NOT WRITE IN THIS MARGIN

9. A garden in the shape of a **right-angled triangle** has a semi-circular pond on the hypotenuse as shown below.

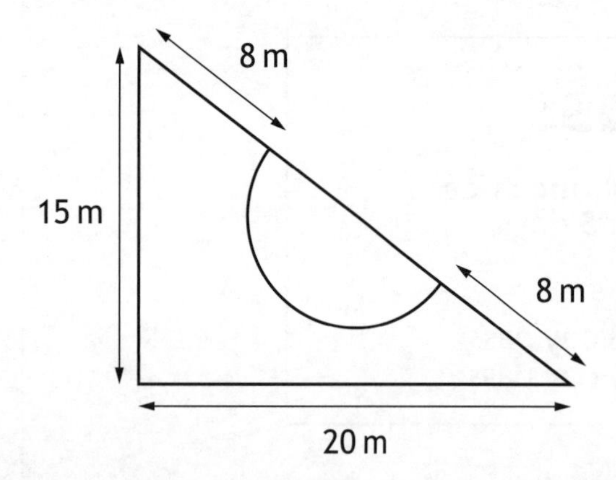

(a) Calculate the diameter of the pond. **2**

(b) The garden, excluding the pond, is to be covered with stone chips.

Calculate the area to be covered with stone chips. **3**

(c) The stone chips come in 25 kg bags costing £2·59 each.

1000 kg of chips covers an area of 20 m^2.

Calculate the cost of the stone chips for the garden. **3**

MARKS | DO NOT WRITE IN THIS MARGIN

10. Brendan makes candles from blocks of wax.

Each block of wax is a cuboid measuring 30 cm by 20 cm by 20 cm as shown.

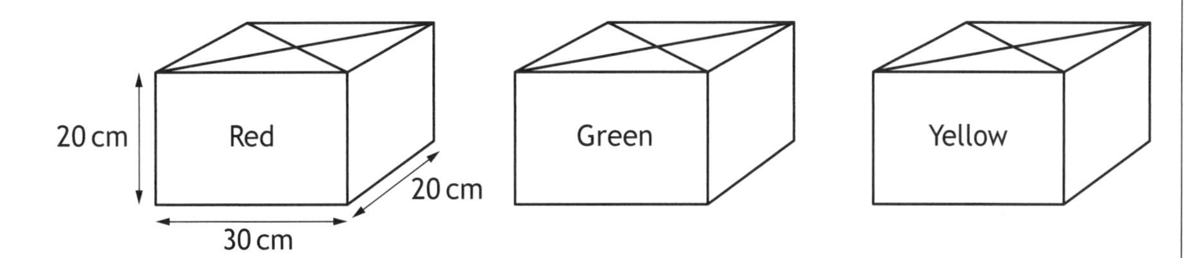

Each candle contains the colours red, green and yellow in the ratio 3 : 1 : 2 respectively.

Each candle is a cube with volume 729 cm^3.

(a) Brendan only has 1 block of each colour.

What is the maximum number of candles that he can make? **3**

(b) Brendan makes the maximum number of candles.

Any wax that is left over is thrown away.

Each block of wax costs £13·75.

Brendan also buys wicks which cost 18p per candle.

Brendan adds 65% to his costs when calculating the selling price of each candle.

What is Brendan's selling price for each candle? **3**

MARKS DO NOT WRITE IN THIS MARGIN

10. (continued)

Brendan also makes blue candles in the shape of a cylinder with a cone on top as shown.

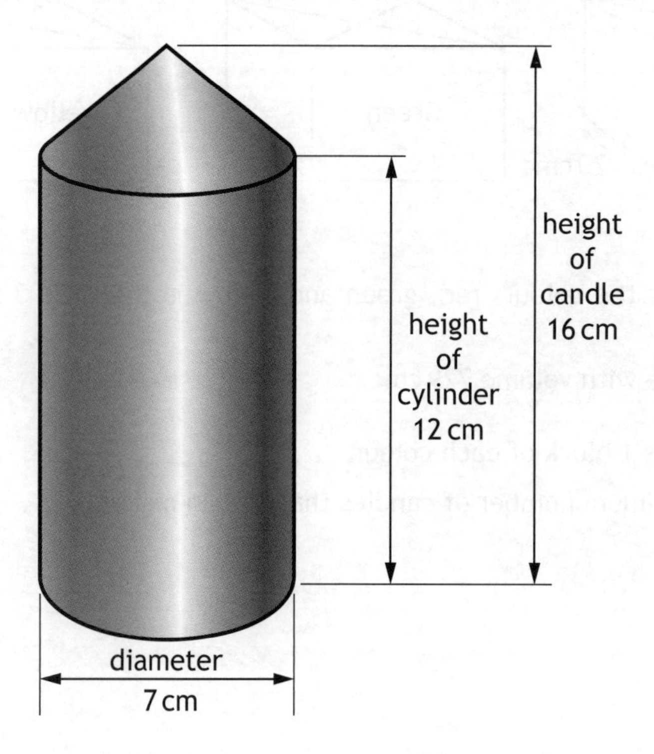

(c) He buys blue wax in blocks with volume 12 000 cm^3.

Brendan thinks that he can make 25 of these candles from one block of wax.

Is he correct?

Use your working to justify your answer. **7**

[END OF SPECIMEN QUESTION PAPER]

MARKS | DO NOT WRITE IN THIS MARGIN

ADDITIONAL SPACE FOR ANSWERS

Additional diagram for Question 4

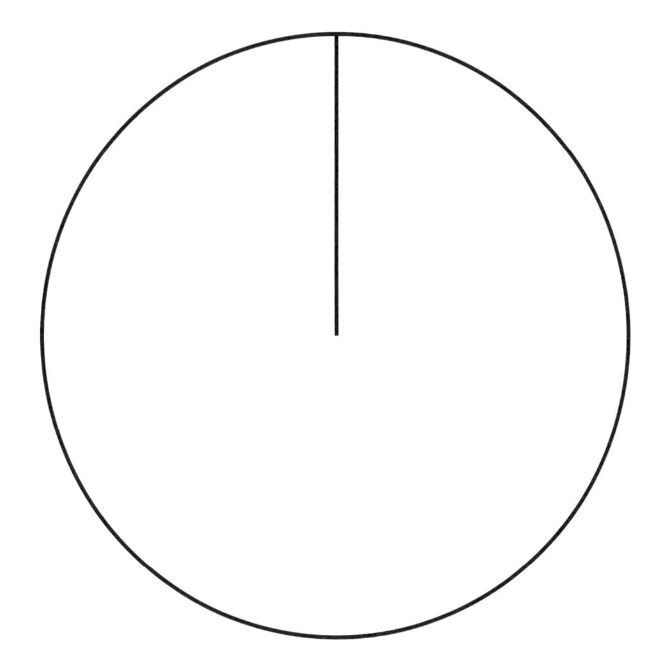

MARKS | DO NOT WRITE IN THIS MARGIN

ADDITIONAL SPACE FOR ANSWERS

Additional diagram for Question 7 (a)

MARKS | DO NOT WRITE IN THIS MARGIN

ADDITIONAL SPACE FOR ANSWERS

MARKS DO NOT WRITE IN THIS MARGIN

ADDITIONAL SPACE FOR ANSWERS

NATIONAL 5

Answers

ANSWERS FOR

SQA NATIONAL 5 LIFESKILLS MATHEMATICS 2017

NATIONAL 5 LIFESKILLS MATHEMATICS 2016

Paper 1

1. 9 kg bag, supported by working

2. $\frac{6}{36}\left(\frac{1}{6}\right)$

3. 0853 (from Biggar)

4. 7 weeks

5. (a) Task letters and times inserted correctly, ie

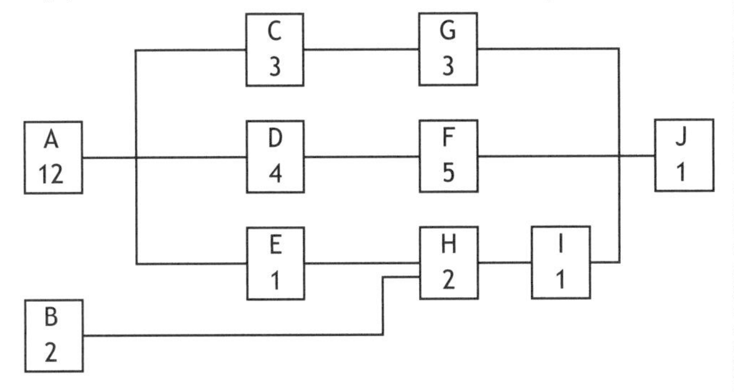

(b) Yes, as it takes 22 months

6. (£)369·95

7. (£)7·26

8. 138 m^2

9. 8 (cm)

10. (a) $\frac{1}{18}$

(b) Yes, $\frac{2}{25} > \frac{2}{36}$

Paper 2

1. (a) Proof, e.g. $\frac{21400}{5347600} \times 100 = 0.4$

or $5347600 \div 100 \times 0{\cdot}4 + 5347600 = 5369000$

(b) 5 433 700

2. 01:30 (on Sunday 10th)

3. Make one valid comment, eg similar proportion chose 'yes' in survey 2; larger proportion chose 'no' in survey 2; smaller proportion chose 'undecided' in survey 2

4. (a) (i) 1:100 000

(ii) 074°, 9·6 km

(b) 23 (minutes)

5. (a) (i) ($)183

(ii) ($)157 supported by working

(b) £1 gives $1·555 or $1 gives £0·643

6. (a) (i) 81·1

(ii) 0·72

(b) Two valid comments, eg on average Goodhold give a faster lap time; lap times with Goodhold are less consistent

(c) 160 (km/hr)

7. (a) (£)1100

(b) (i) (£)418

(ii) 6·1(%)

(c) Premier bank, 24 months

8. (a) 32 candles

(b) (£)2·43 or 2·42

(c) No, he can't make 25 candles, supported by working

NATIONAL 5 LIFESKILLS MATHEMATICS 2017

One mark is available for each •. There are no half marks.

Paper 1

1. • $(194 - 2) \times 50$
   • 9600 (mm)
2. (a) • Strategy: know how to calculate 2·5% of £6000
   • Calculate 2·5% of £6000: 150
   • Add commission to basic salary: (£)2600

   (b) • Strategy: attempt to calculate gross pay – total deductions
   • (£)1870·39
3. (a) • Communication: 4 points correct
   • Communication: all 6 points correct

D	0	60	120	160	200	260
W	40	110	130	175	220	275

   (b) Line of best fit

   (c) Answer consistent with line of best fit (days)

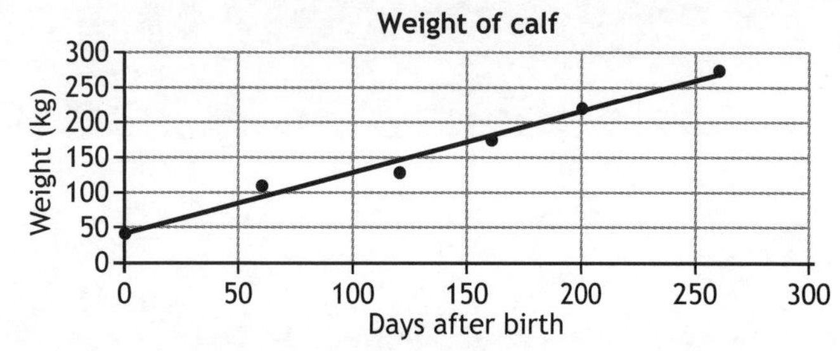

4. • 1·6/8
   • 4/20 (3/20 does not need to be explicitly stated) or 8/40 and 6/40 or 0·2 and 0·15 or equivalent
   • No, supported by working
5. (a) $10 \times 14 + 1 = 141$, she needs bands D and A

   (b) • Calculate cost for shop 1: 49·50
   • Calculate cost for shop 2: 45·48
   • Conclusion consistent with working: Shop 2

   OR
   • Calculate discount for 1 shop: 26·30 or 30·32 or 27·81
   • Calculate discount for remaining two shops
   • Conclusion consistent with working: Shop 2
6. • Calculate one (£1) share: $2\ 794\ 000 \div 8 = 349\ 250$
   • Calculate total number of shares: $2·50 + 2·00 + 4·00 + 0·50 = 9$
   • Calculate the total amount: $9 \times 698\ 500 =$ (£)6 286 500

   OR
   • Calculate one (50p) share: $2\ 794\ 000 \div 8 = 349\ 250$
   • Calculate total number of shares: $1 + 4 + 5 + 8 = 18$
   • Calculate total amount: $18 \times 349\ 250 =$ (£)6 286 500

   OR
   • Calculate the amount for any teacher other than Mr Young: Miss Smith 1 397 000 or Mr Jones 349 250 or Mr Ross 1 746 250
   • Calculate the amount for another teacher: either of the remaining two
   • Calculate amount for final teacher and total amount: $1\ 397\ 000 + 349\ 250 + 1\ 746\ 250 + 2\ 794\ 000 = 6\ 286\ 500$
7. (a) • Strategy: know how to calculate composite area
   • 20 (cm^2)

   (b) • Calculate the number of badges per pack: $180 \div 20 = 9$
   • Calculate the cost of enamel for one badge: $90 \div 9 = 10$
   • Calculate selling price: $10 + 3 + 17 =$ (£)30

   OR
   • Calculate the number of badges per pack: $180 \div 20 = 9$
   • Calculate the total cost of 9 badges: $9 \times 3 + 9 \times 17 + 90 = 270$
   • Calculate selling price: $270 \div 9 =$ (£)30
8. • Identify the blood groups that B+ can help: e.g. AB+ and B+
   • Interpret stacked bar chart: 3 people AB+ and 9 people B+
   • Calculate fraction: $\frac{3+9}{100} = \frac{12}{100}\left(= \frac{3}{25}\right)$
9. (a) • Correct substitution in Pythagoras' Theorem: e.g. $10^2 - 6^2$
   • Calculate the missing side: $x = 8$
   • Calculate the length of the semi-circle: $3·14 \times 6 \div 2 = 9·42$
   • Calculate the perimeter of the shape: $10 + 8 + 9·42 = 27·42$(cm)

   (b) • Strategy: know how to calculate area of rectangular strip
   • $(27·42 - 0·3) \times \frac{1}{2} = 13·56$

Paper 2

1. • Strategy: know how to calculate the volume of half a cylinder
   • $\frac{1}{2} \times \pi \times 7^2 \times 30$
   • 2309·07...cm^3

   OR
   • Strategy: know to calculate the area of the semi-circle and multiply it by 30
   • $\frac{1}{2} \times \pi \times 7^2$
   • $= 76·96... \times 30 = 2309·07...\ cm^3$
2. (a) • Work out the cost of 8000 shares: $8000 \times 0·73 = 5840$
   • Calculate percentage decrease: evidence of 0·97
   • Calculate percentage increase: evidence of 1·042
   • Identify power: $...^2$
   • Calculate the value of the shares: (£)6150·64

   OR
   • Calculate percentage decrease: evidence of 0·97
   • Calculate percentage increase: evidence of 1·042
   • Identify power: $...^2$
   • Calculate the value of 1 share: 0·768...
   • Calculate the value of 8000 shares: (£)6150·64

   (b) • Calculate $\frac{5}{8}$ of 6560 and subtract commission
   • Calculate amount received: (£)4087·05

3. • Calculate new price: 1260 + 151·20 = 1411·20
   • Calculate the deposit: $\frac{1}{3}$ of 14 11·20 = 470·40
   • Calculate the amount still payable:
     470·40 + 200 = 670·40
     1411·20 − 670·40 = 740·80
   • State how much each monthly payment is:
     740·80 ÷ 8 = (£)92·60

4. (a) 71
   (b) • Calculate either median: 61 or 71
       • Calculate other median and difference: 71 − 61 = 10
   (c) • Calculate lower quartile: Q_1 = 67
       • Calculate upper quartile: Q_3 = 84
       • Correct end points drawn: 59 and 95
       • Consistent box drawn: box showing Q_1, Q_2 and Q_3

5. (a) • Calculate the distance from a scale drawing:
         8 × 3000000 = 24000000
       • Give answer in kilometres:
         24000000 ÷ 100 ÷ 1000 = 240(km)
   (b) • Calculate average speed and change hours and minutes to hours: $\frac{240}{7.5}$ = ...
       • Convert average speed into knots: ... × 0·54 = ...
       • Calculate average speed to 2 significant figures:
         17·28 = 17 (2 sig fig)
   (c) • know how to calculate amount of euro: 55% of 2400 × 1·15 ...
       • calculate remaining euro: 1518 − 1379 = 139 (euro)
   (d) (i) • state probability $\frac{7}{32}$
       (ii) • calculate denominator of 28
            • state probability $\frac{1}{28}$

6. (a) • Strategy: know to calculate two arrangements
       • Calculate one arrangement:
         2·25m ÷ 0·75 = 3 cages
         15m ÷ 0·85 = 17 cages
         Total = 3 × 17 × 2 = 102 cages
       • Calculate second arrangement and make consistent conclusion:
         2·25m ÷ 0·85 = 2 cages
         15m ÷ 0·75 = 20 cages exactly
         Total = 20 × 2 × 2 = 80
   (b) • Calculate basic pay: $1\frac{1}{2}$ × 14·40 = 21·60
       • Calculate overtime pay: $8\frac{1}{2}$ × 14·40 × 1·5 = 183·60
       • Calculate weekly gross pay: (183·60 + 21·60) × 5
         = 205·20 × 5
         = (£)1026

       OR

       • Calculate 10 hours basic pay: 10 × 14·40 = 144
       • Calculate $8\frac{1}{2}$ hours at $\frac{1}{2}$ time: $8\frac{1}{2}$ × 7·20 = 61·20
       • Calculate weekly gross pay:
         (144 + 61·20) × 5 = (£)1026

7. (a) (i) • (24 + 22 + 19 + 18 + 17 + 17) ÷ 6 = 19·5(°)
       (ii) • Calculate $(x - \bar{x})^2$: 20·25,6·25,0·25,2·25,6·25,6·25
            • Substitute into formula: $\sqrt{(41.5 \div 5)}$
            • Calculate standard deviation: 2·88
   (b) Two valid comments
       • 1 mark for comment regarding mean, e.g. on average Durban's temperatures are higher
       • 1 mark for comment regarding standard deviation, e.g. Durban's temperatures are less consistent
   (c) • Strategy/process: calculate one local time
       • Calculate the other two local times: Mumbai 9:00pm
         London: 1:30pm
         New York: 8:30am
       • State offices that can take part: New York and London

       OR

       • Strategy/process: calculate one time difference
       • Calculate remaining two time differences:
         Mumbai + 5h 30mins
         London −2h
         New York −7h
       • State offices that can take part: New York and London

       OR

       • Calculate how long until 3:30pm: 22 hours 5 minutes
       • Calculate local times: Mumbai 9:00pm
         London: 1:30pm
         New York: 8:30am
       • State offices that can take part: New York and London

8. (a) • Calculate short sides of triangle: 500
       • Show evidence of the correct form of Pythagoras' theorem: $500^2 + 500^2$
       • Calculate length of hypotenuse of triangle:
         707·1068... = 707 (mm)
   (b) • Calculate the area of the square encasing pentagonal shower base and subtract area of missing triangle: $900^2 - \frac{1}{2} \times 500 \times 500$
       • Calculate area of pentagonal base:
         810000 − 125000 = 685000 (mm²)
   (c) • Strategy: evidence of quarter circle added to rectangles
       • Calculate the area of the quarter circle:
         $\frac{1}{4} \times \pi \times 600 \times 600 = 282743$
       • 282743 + 450000 = 732743
       • Zuzanna should pick the offset quadrant (since 732743 mm² > 685000 mm²)

       OR

       • Strategy: evidence of whole square minus area that is not part of the base.
       • Calculate the area of the quarter circle:
         $\frac{1}{4} \times \pi \times 600 \times 600 = 282743$
       • 810000 − (360000 − 282743) = 732743
       • Zuzanna should pick the offset quadrant (since 732743 mm² > 685000 mm²)

NATIONAL 5 LIFESKILLS MATHEMATICS 2017 SPECIMEN QUESTION PAPER

One mark is available for each •. There are no half marks.

Paper 1

1. • Strategy: Add flight time and time zone
• 7:30pm

2. • Identify correct values 9 and 66
• $\frac{3}{22}$

3. • Strategy: know to use upper/lower limits
• $\frac{17}{20} = 85\%$
• No, as 85% < 88%

OR

• Strategy: know to use upper/lower limits
• $\frac{3}{20} = 15\%$
• No, as 15% > 12%

OR

• Strategy: know to use upper/lower limits
• 88% of 20 = 17·6, ie need 18
• No, as only 17 in tolerance, so batch fails

4. Ans: (£)7·26
• Strategy: pick correct band F
• 76·13 and 145
• 2 × 76·13 − 145 = 7·26

5. (a) • Boys, with valid reason
(b) • State the median: 26
• State the quartiles: 18,30
(c)

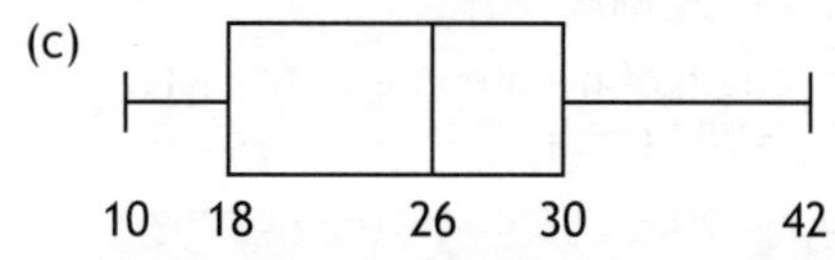

• Strategy: end points at 10 and 42
• Strategy: box showing Q_1, Q_2, Q_3

6. • Calculate basic and overtime hours: 40 and 6
• Calculate overtime: 6 × 1·5 × 15·60 = 140·40
• Calculate gross weekly pay: 15·60 × 40 + 140·40 = (£)764·40

7. • Strategy: know to divide by 30 then multiply by 4·96
• 1500 ÷ 30 = 50
50 × 4·96 = 248 (Zloty)

8. • Strategy: know to add fractions
• $\frac{1}{6} + \frac{2}{5} = \frac{5}{30} + \frac{12}{30} = \frac{17}{30}$
• $\frac{13}{30}$ or equivalent

9. • Strategy: know how to find the time for 4 bakers
• 3 × 5 ÷ 4 = 3·75
• 3 hours 45 minutes

10. (a) (i) • Strategy: four points plotted correctly
• Strategy: remaining three points plotted correctly
(ii) • Acceptable line of best fit drawn
(b) • Strategy: extend line of best fit and read graph
• No, as the height will only be 2·36 metres at 0830

11. • 200 × 2·75 = 550
• £13·75
• 550 − 13·75 = 536·25
• 700 − 536·25 = £163·75

12. • $\frac{15}{200}$
• Strategy: know how to compare gradients
• $\frac{15}{200} = 0{\cdot}075$
• Yes, 0·06 < 0·075 < 0·08

13. (a) • Strategy: know to add semi-circle and 3 straight edges
• $\frac{1}{2} \times 3{\cdot}14 \times 20 + 20 + 8 + 8 = 67{\cdot}4$
• 67·4 × 5 × 3 = (£)1011
(b) • Strategy: any 7 boxes correct
• Strategy: remaining 4 boxes correct
(c) • Strategy: select critical path 2 + 4 + 2 + 1 + 2 + 1
• No, because it will take 12 hours

Paper 2

1. • Strategy: identify multiplier 0·959
• Strategy: identify power ...^{3}
• Calculate value 687939·7816
• (£)688 000

2. • $\frac{24}{64}$ or equivalent
• Mark on gauge consistent with working

3. (a) (i) • $(\bar{x} =) 48{\cdot}7$
(ii) • Process: calculate $(x - \bar{x})^2$ 0·81, 0·16, 2·25, 0·64, 3·24, 0·64
• Strategy: substitute into formula $\sqrt{\frac{7{\cdot}74}{5}}$
• Calculate standard deviation (s =) 1·24
(b) Two valid comments:
• Comment regarding the mean: on average, the athlete's times have increased after training with the coach.
• Comment regarding standard deviation: the athlete's times are more consistent after training with the coach.

4. • Strategy/process: interpret graph and state fraction for each type of car $\frac{30}{150}, \frac{65}{150}, \frac{55}{150}$ or equivalent
• Calculate angles 72°, 156°, 132°
• Construct pie chart and complete with labels

5. (a) • Strategy: consider three options
- 210 or 210 or 252
- 252 (boxes)

(b) • £1755 + 252 × £2·99 = £2508·48
- £2508·48 ÷ 252 ÷ 4 = £2·49

6. (a) • 0·12 × (42380 – 8060) = 4118·40
- 0·02 × (49920 – 42380) = 150·80
- 4118·40 + 150·80 = 4269·20

(b) • 0·09 × 49920 = 4492·80
- 49920 – (4492·80 + 4269·20 + 6870·04) = 34287·96
- (34287·96 ÷ 12) = 2857·33

(c) • 2857·33 – (750 + 450 + 625 + 125 + 350) = 557·33
- Yes, he will have enough.

7. (a) • 22 ÷ 5 = 4·4 cm
37÷ 5 = 7·4 cm
- Bearing of 045°(±1°) measured correctly and 4·4 cm(±0·1 cm) correctly drawn
- Bearing of 170°(±1°) measured correctly and 7·4 cm(±0·1 cm) correctly drawn

(b) • 314 (°)
- 6·1 cm so 30·5 miles

(c) • 30·5 + 22 + 37 = 89·5
- 8 hour 30 min – 4 hour 5 min = 4 hour 25 min

$4\frac{25}{60} = 4{\cdot}416...$

- $\frac{89{\cdot}5}{4{\cdot}416...} = 20{\cdot}264...$ 20·26 mph

8. (a) (i) • Strategy: identify the costs not included \$32 and \$37
- \$114 + 32 + 37 = \$183

(ii) • Strategy: identify the "missing" attraction and the two cheapest attractions \$24, \$32 and \$30
- Calculate the cost for card 2: \$71 + \$24 + \$32 + \$30 = \$157
- State cost of card 3: \$180
- \$157

(b) • Strategy: evidence of knowing to divide: 157 ÷ 100·96 or 100·96 ÷ 157
- £1 gives \$1·555 or \$1 gives £0·643

9. (a) • Strategy/process: use Pythagoras Theorem to calculate hypotenuse 25
- 25 – 16 = 9(m)

(b) • Strategy: triangle – semi circle
- $\frac{1}{2} \times \pi \times 4{\cdot}5^2 = 31{\cdot}808...$
- $150 - 31{\cdot}808... = 118{\cdot}191...118{\cdot}2(m^2)$

(c) • 118·2 ÷ 20 × 1000 = 5910
- 5910 ÷ 25 = 236·4, 237 bags
- 237 × 2·59 = (£)613·83

10. (a) • Strategy: know how to use ratio
- 12000 + 4000 + 8000 = 24000 cm^3
- 24000 ÷ 729 = 32·92... = 32 (candles)

OR

- Strategy: know how to use ratio
- 12000 cm^3 and 364·5
- 12000 ÷ 364·5 = 32·92 rounded to 32 (candles)

(b) • 3 × 13·75 + 32 × 0·18 = 47·01
- 47·01 × 1·65 = 77·57
- 77·57 ÷ 32 = 2·424... = (£)2·43/2.42

(c) • Strategy: knows how to find compound volume
- Strategy: substitute into cylinder formula $V = \pi \times 3{\cdot}5 \times 3{\cdot}5 \times 12$
- 461·8 (or 461·58)
- Strategy: substitute into cone formula $V = \frac{1}{3}\pi \times 3{\cdot}5 \times 3{\cdot}5 \times 4$
- 51·3
- 461·8 + 51·3 = 513·1,12000 ÷ 513·1 = 23·38
- No, he can't make 25 candles

Acknowledgements

Permission has been sought from all relevant copyright holders and Hodder Gibson is grateful for the use of the following:

An image of a timetable adapted from 'Stagecoach Dumfries – Edinburgh Bus Timetable' © Stagecoach Group (2016 Paper 1 page 4);
Image © MiloVad/Shutterstock.com (2016 Paper 2 page 10);
Image © Aleksander Krsmanovic/Shutterstock.com (2017 Paper 2 page 5);
Image © topae/Shutterstock.com (2017 Paper 2 page 10);
Image © Jodie Johnson/stock.adobe.com (2017 Paper 2 page 14);
Image © Baloncici/Shutterstock.com (2017 Paper 2 page 15);
Image © ibreakstock/Shutterstock.com (SQP, Paper 1 page 3);
Image © eugenesergeev/stock.adobe.com (SQP, Paper 2 page 7).